A Kepi in the Tide

Hobart M. Walker — ca 1860

A Kepi in the Tide

By

John Ickes

Contents

Dedication

To the best person I've ever known – my cherished wife Vonia. With her, Heather and Rebecca sustaining this effort, it's been a joy. For Sage, Keira and Michael – I really hope this gives you some insight into one of our ancestors, and a very special man.

Acknowledgements

This effort included the active and enthusiastic participation of many, many people, making it impossible to thank everyone by name. At the same time, the contributions by some are so significant that without them, it simply would not have happened, and my inadequate but very sincere thanks go to:

Kay Martin and Jim Adams – Walker cousins, very fine people, and unimaginably generous in their time, talent, resources and encouragement. This is really for all of us who share the Walker connection.

Lauran Greathouse Strait and Jeff Andrews – editors, writers and friends. Their oh-so-patient and candid suggestions and guidance have moved this from an idea to a manuscript. I owe you!

Travis Gilbert at the Cape Fear Historical Society for a spontaneous and comprehensive study on Wilmington, The Cape Fear River and people of the era.

Captain Carl Marshburn of Wilmington, NC. A gentleman with an encyclopedic knowledge of the Cape Fear River, and a kind willingness to share it.

Bob Langston – *artiste extraordinaire* and cheerleader for this and so many other projects.

Wayne Mori – archivist at Saint Paul's Episcopal Cathedral, Buffalo, NY. The source of so much information on the Walkers of Buffalo. Without him we may never have met Clara.

Introduction and Prologue

This began as a simple genealogical exercise. Checking the boxes on the family tree, I drew a blank at the brother of my great-grandfather, Dr. Jerome Walker of Brooklyn, NY. I was aware that his parents, Ferdinand and Elmira Walker, had a total of twelve children of which, sadly, only five lived beyond their teens. It was one of these, my great-great-uncle Hobart, that quickly drew my attention.

There wasn't too much extraordinary about Hobart, at least as I could learn in the early stages of our acquaintance. A few sparse items in widely-spaced publications, but not much else, at least until 1861.

At that point, references to a "Hobart Walker" became more plentiful, but didn't seem to relate to the same person, as they covered a number of years and several different locations. It wasn't until I began to piece these elements together that a larger story began to emerge.

Hobart, it seems, was an adventuresome, idealistic young man, and when the Civil War erupted, it was not surprising that he, like so many others, felt called to the colors. What did seem different was the extent he went to serve. Between 1861 and 1865 he served in a total of five different units, was (sequentially) a Private, a Sergeant, a Lieutenant, a Private and ultimately a Corporal. He was wounded twice and a prisoner of war. All that notwithstanding, he kept returning to the service of his country. It was that story that made him such a compelling figure for me and made it important for me to tell his tale.

The events depicted in this book are, for the most part, true and documented. Where possible, I've used letters, diary entries, unit histories and newspaper accounts to "flesh out" the story. The narrative is of my own creation, as are a few minor scenes, but are, I feel, logical and I use them only to move the story along. If there are errors, they are my own. If there is a hero – and I believe there certainly is – it is my great-great uncle, Hobart M. Walker.

Chapter 1

Buffalo, New York, May 1861

His nose itched, but he struggled to ignore it and remain motionless. In the buttery sun of an early May morning, Private Hobart Walker and sixty-three other recruits of Company H, Seventy-Fourth New York Militia stood in line. And waited.

"What can they possibly be talking about, that takes so long?" A soft voice behind him mumbled. Hobart shook his head just a bit, side to side. The voice continued.

"Been up since six. Standing here – what – an hour? We're here in the sun – they're in the shade. Isn't right."

Oh, that itches – why are they taking so long?

Five officers stood in the shade of the crenelated tower of Fort Porter and talked. One tossed his hands about in wild gestures while the others stood still. Hobart felt the sweat running down his neck.

"Coffee for breakfast. I will need a necessary shortly." A new voice joined in, barely audible.

At last the group of officers broke up and rejoined the lines of men. The one who had done most of the gesturing walked up to them.

"Men, this morning we shall practice the drills you learned yesterday and then begin a new subject – bayonet drill"

Bayonet drill ... we don't HAVE bayonets. We don't even have uniforms — not all of us.

Hobart glanced along the line of men. Most of them wore their civilian clothing, while here and there a man stood, sometimes in a soldiers' trousers, shirt, coat and hat and sometimes in the army coat and hat, but their civilian trousers. The Seventy-Fourth Militia would need some time before they were ready to go to war.

With a dramatic wave of his saber and a deep-throated "Forward," the company commander stepped off, and the lines of men followed. Hobart and the others tried gamely to keep in step with each other and turn, pivot, wheel or reverse as the orders poured back from the Captain. Hundreds of marching feet had long-since crushed the grass to dust on Fort Porter's parade field, but Hobart didn't think they looked much like soldiers. Not yet.

At the stentorian command, "Halt!" the lines stopped.

"Present arms!" Hobart looked at the man to his right. The man looked back. When the soldier on his left brought his musket off his shoulder and held it upright, the others, in a wavering line, did the same.

Hobart studied the musket in his hands. The barrel was pitted and dull. The wooden stock had numerous nicks in it, and the trigger guard showed unmistakable signs of wear. Growing up in Brooklyn, he had little experience with rifles, but he remembered the long-barreled gun that had hung over Grandfather Smith's fireplace back in Butternuts.

"My grandfather was a hunter and fought in the War of 1812. We loved his stories ... battles ... hunting bear ... " He hefted the rifle. "Wouldn't think much of this thing." The other young men nodded.

Holding the musket upright, he slid his thumb up to the hammer and tried to pull it back, as he'd seen his grandfather do any number of times. It didn't budge. He tried harder, but it still didn't move – at all. He glanced down. The two jaws of the lock held no flint between them.

I couldn't load this thing if the entire Confederate Army was charging at me.

* * *

Hobart had not been in Buffalo long, having moved there the previous autumn. He'd finished his school and had found a position in Buffalo with a friend of his father's brother Stephen. He was boarding with his uncle and family but wrote regularly to his parents back home in Brooklyn.

There had been a torrent of correspondence between Buffalo and Brooklyn as Hobart tried to convince his father that enlisting was the proper thing to do. Ferdinand was not in favor of the idea, and he said so.

He could wait no longer for Ferdinand's blessing. At the table in his uncle's dining room, he wrote:

Buffalo, April 24, 1861

Dear Father,

I received your very welcome letter yesterday. I had not actually enlisted and did not intend to until I heard from you although I had spoken for a place. I am now a member of a regiment 74 – Company H. The captain is Addison Root, a cousin of Charles and a real good man.

Everybody says it is the best regiment and one of the best companies in the place. There are several good churchmen in the company, two or three ministers' sons and two young organists. One of the Sergeants, a friend of mine, had promised to give me some outside drilling and to get me the position of Corporal shortly.

To be sure, as you say it is not everyone's duty to go, but at the same time I think those ought to go who sacrifice the least. There is no one dependent on me.

As to my health I think can I "get along" with that first-rate now. I sacrifice nothing at all of any account and I think it is much better for me to go than for a man to leave his family at home.

I had not hardly decided to go until I heard Dr. Shelton preach last Sunday and he put it down so forcibly that from that time I made up my mind to go.

Love to all and believe me as ever your

Affectionate son,
Hobart

That had been some weeks ago, and now he was a soldier. Captain Root had seen to it that he was grouped with young men of whom he was confident Ferdinand would approve.

True to his word, Hobart applied himself to the job of shedding the skin of a mercantile clerk and becoming a warrior. He and his new-found colleagues spent days going through what seemed to be an endless repetition of formations, marching and movement.

"Shoulder, arms!" and "Guard against infantry, guard!". They formed lines and marched. They stopped and started again. They grew stronger and more confident. The soldiers opened ranks and they closed them.

Standing down, they lounged in the shadow of the fort, grateful for the cool breezes that eddied in from Lake Erie.

"I counted them, you know," Tom Wallace, an eighteen-year old from Port Jervis, said.

"You counted what?"

"I counted all the different rifles in the company. There are twelve different types of rifles among us. Twelve! Different calibers. Different sizes. How can we fight the Secesh with this?"

The evenings were generally free time for the young troopers, who happily filled them with card games, a little music, and a little less reading. Hobart sought out Sergeant James Adams, a man he knew from Mr. Walsh's business. In the twilight, they reviewed together what they had practiced in the day.

"Left Dress! "Open Ranks! Close Ranks! Right About, March!" Then they did it all again. And again.

I think I'm beginning to look like a soldier.

4

"Fall in!" They aligned themselves in rows. Rows that now were straight and evenly spaced.

"Forward, march!" In unison, they stepped off. Across the parade field they marched until they came to the supply barn. "Halt!"

Hobart and the others were issued underwear, socks, trousers, coats and hats. The hat fascinated him. It was different from anything he'd ever seen. Flat-topped and leather-brimmed, it sat comfortably on his head.

"What do they call these things?"

"Kepi. It's a kepi – like the French wear, I think."

Another voice chimed in.

"It's a forage cap, you dunce. Everyone knows that."

"Kepi, forage cap … it's the same deuced thing"

"Dunce"

"Thickhead"

A shiny brass badge, the crossed rifles of the infantry, pinned to the front added the perfect finishing touch. He looked in a mirror, and he smiled.

July came, and with it the stifling, humid cauldron of summer.

"Leave your coats in the barracks," shouted the sergeants, and the soldiers smiled weary smiles. Still, as Hobart and the others in the Seventy-Fourth drilled, the sweat poured from their faces and marked their shirts in dark, irregular blotches. Drills continued through the summer days and Hobart came to loath the bugle blasts that called them to the parade ground.

Amid the heat, the sweat and the drilling, the recruits received bad news from the front. Hobart returned from a visit to his uncle with a newspaper under his arm. The headline said it all – "Union forces routed at Manassas". In the barracks, they gathered around him. The air was thick and tense.

"What does that mean?"

"It means, I suppose, that our boys came up against the Rebs and got whipped."

"Where's Manassas?"

"Virginia. North part, I think."

"Did we lose the war?" There was fear on many faces.

"No, nothing like that. It will just take longer than we thought. A lot longer."

The one bright spot came in three large, lumbering, horse drawn dray wagons. Captain Root had the company fall in and they marched to the armory. While the Quartermaster Sergeant watched them from his perch atop a stack of heavy wooden crates, the soldiers stacked the collection of rifles and muskets they had carried since April.

The rumors had been percolating for several weeks, but unlike so many tales that proved to be empty, this time there was something to it. There were rifles in those crates. New rifles. The word raced through the company.

Springfield Model 55's! Percussion cap rifles!

The barrels were bright and without flaw. The maple stocks were shiny, the varnish smooth.

They looked deadly.

"Come on, boys, step it up. Sign right here." The sergeants and corporals scurried around the milling soldiers. Rifles in hand, they moved to a fourth wagon.

"Bayonets, lads. Real ones. Get 'em in those scabbards. We'll drill with them tomorrow."

With the arrival of the new weapons, target practice became an additional part of the day's routine. Boys who had hunted from the time they could walk and boys who had never fired a weapon learned to load, aim, fire and then clean the black powder weapons.

"You look like a miner, coming up out of the ground."

When Company H returned from the firing lines, faces and hands black from gunpowder, the insults flew. Now the days were punctuated by the ongoing crackle of rifle fire on the ranges.

Hobart stepped up to the firing line. Ten soldiers stood to the left of him, nine to the right. Each had the heavy Springfield musket on their right shoulder. They strained to hear the sergeant.

"Load in nine times – Load!" Hands lowered the weapon to the ground.

"Handle cartridge!" Hobart reached into the leather pouch on his belt, withdrew a paper-wrapped cartridge, and put it between his teeth.

"Tear – cartridge!" He ripped the tube open and flecks of black powder flew.

"Charge - cartridge!" The powder streamed into the muzzle and down the barrel. He held the paper, empty of powder but with the hard lead bullet still within, waiting.

"Draw – rammer!" The long, thin rammer slid out from its place beneath the barrel.

"Ram – cartridge!" Twice Hobart slammed the rammer down the barrel, forcing the round to the end and packing it against the powder.

"Return – rammer" – The thin rod snaked out of the barrel. His right hand grasped the stock at the trigger, his left the barrel.

"Prime!" Pulled back the hammer. Reached into the cap box and extracted a primer cap. Thumbed it down onto the nipple, over the trigger.

He held the rifled musket, loaded with the deadly lead slug and primed to fire.

"Ready!" He raised the musket and held it directly in front of him, muzzle up, stock down.

"Aim" With the butt of the rifle pressed tight against his right shoulder, he slid his fingertip over the trigger and sighted down the barrel.

"Fire!" Squeezed the trigger, and the musket boomed. It kicked into his shoulder and a mushroom of white smoke exploded from the muzzle.

They repeated the drill. And again. Over and over, until his shoulder was bruised and aching, his face and hands covered with acrid black soot. When they began, a round would sometimes strike the target, a hundred yards away. More often it missed, leaving the mark pristine. Days of firing turned into weeks and the white paper circles became riddled with bullet holes striking the center. They were learning how to kill.

A very young private burst through the door, into the barracks. His right hand against his chest, he struggled to catch his breath, his eyes shining. Finally, through gasps, he spoke:

"They're here! We're going to get 'em them in the morning!" he blurted.

"They?"

The young soldier could barely contain his elation

"The new uniforms! Zouaves!" With that, the entire mess leapt to their feet and crowded around. Questions flew like the gnats of a Buffalo summer.

"Where are they? When shall we get them? Have you seen them? What are the colors?"

Next to orders to march against Richmond, this might have been the most exciting thing they could have heard.

There was pandemonium in the barracks. Uniform trousers and jackets flung in heaps, hats and boots scattered. Above it all, the exhilarated chatter of youth.

"These trousers! I ain't ever seen anything so red!"

"Don't these coats beat all? Truly fizzing! And them gaiters!"

"What's this thing? Where's it go?"

"It's called a fez, you coot! It's a hat – you put it on top of your ignorant head!"

"Who you callin' a coot?"

"We need a parade, boys – this time we really need a parade. Those girls will think we're really a circumstance when we get all slicked up!"

"Those Johnny Rebs will take one look at us and run like rabbits."

Buffalo photographers were besieged with dozens of young soldiers eager to secure an image of themselves in their dashing attire, a cartes de visite, to send back to doting parents and more than one young woman. Hobart considered this, then thought he'd save the money.

Perhaps later.

The scorching summer wore on, turning faces and hands copper and leathery. Soldiers sweltered in their layers of flannel and wool. Hobart felt a growing, insistent restlessness. He and the others in Company H were becoming adept at the drills, and their riflery improved with each round fired. Still, he had a mounting sense of impatience, a rising urge to go somewhere – to do something.

"When d'you suppose we'll actually go anywhere?" A private from West Seneca looked up from the boots he was cleaning.

A voice came from the corner of the room. "Could be any day. I reckon we're as ready as we're going to be."

"Those other companies left back in May, and we're still here. I didn't enlist to protect Buffalo."

"Be patient, sonny. The Secesh are just as like to come sneaking down from Canada as you are to go to Richmond. Just be patient."

* * *

The captain held his sabre perfectly straight before him, sunlight flashing from the polished blade. Ninety-seven soldiers in dark blue were perfectly aligned in rows of six, Lieutenants ahead of Sergeants, Corporals in front of Privates. At the command, they stepped off, almost as one, and marched with arrogant precision across the parade grounds, past the magazine and the Old Castle. The bridge over the Erie Canal rumbled as they crossed, brogans thundering on the deck boards. An impatient train wheezed at the Buffalo and Niagara Falls Railroad depot. They were going to war.

Hobart and Lemuel Christian, another Buffalo youth, watched as they paraded past.

"Who are they?" Lemuel asked.

"Not certain … Company D, I think."

"Where are they headed? Looking all dressed up for drill, I'm thinking."

"Headed out. I heard someone might be going down to Baltimore. Guess it's them."

Christian kicked at the dust.

"It's always someone else. When are we going to go somewhere? Someone ought to take this up with Captain Root."

Hobart snorted. "Not much chance of that. Captain has taken a transfer. Left the fort yesterday."

The two soldiers watched the procession until it was lost to sight.

"C'mon, Lemuel, we have company drill this morning."

*   *   *

Not long after the disheartening news of Manassas, another rumor circulated through Fort Porter. A new regiment was being raised, they said, one to honor a New York officer shot down in Alexandria. Men would be drawn from every town in New York, and it would be an elite unit. One that was certain to go right into action.

Wonder if I could transfer? Get out of Buffalo and see some activity.

This plan spread throughout New York. Hobart was on a furlough away from the camp, relaxing with his Uncle Stephen and the family, when he read about the regiment in the Buffalo newspaper. As he read, there was a knock on the door and Uncle Stephen opened it. In stepped Mr. Gray, an editor at the Buffalo "Enquirer", the newspaper in Hobart's hand. Without preface, Gray strode over to him.

"You've seen the article, have you, lad?" he enquired.

Hobart nodded.

"That's you, you know. You are precisely the soldier they want, and I think you should be Buffalo's representative. This regiment is sure to be at the front, and will be covered in glory before this war is over – which won't be long, I assure you! I've spoken with many others and they agree that you should represent us."

Hobart thought about it.

"I'm really from Brooklyn, you know, not Buffalo."

"A trifle! You're Buffalo now, son!".

Hobart glanced his uncle, who hadn't said anything during the entire exchange. He hadn't had much of a chance – Mr. Gray was an explosive speaker.

He shrugged and said, "You'd certainly do us proud, Hobart."

There was a silence.

"Well," murmured the soldier, "If the Captain would have me transferred, I'd find it an honor."

"Done!" Gray crowed. "I'll talk to him in the morning! Pack your gear, son, you're going to Albany!"

Chapter 2

Upstate New York, August 1861

His head jerked upright and his eyes flew open. He glanced around, confused for a moment, rubbing his eyes. The train was still moving, cars rocking with a gentle rhythm. A sudden flash of brilliant white light made him squint, and a loud thunderclap rocked the car.

Thunderstorm.

Steady rain streaked the windows outside. Hobart stretched and looked around the car. Not many passengers – maybe a dozen. All young men, too, he noticed. A few, like him, wore uniforms, but the others were dressed in work clothes. Two wore suits. He and three of them had boarded the train in Buffalo the previous evening, and the others had, he supposed, boarded along the way while he slept. He guessed that they were all headed the same way – to Albany, to join the Forty-Fourth New York Volunteer Infantry – "Ellsworth's Avengers."

* * *

Transferring from the Seventy-Fourth was easier than he had thought. Captain Root had relocated to a cavalry unit in May, and his replacement signed Hobart's request without any discussion. Transfer in hand, Hobart said goodbye to the Seventy-Fourth, Uncle Stephen and his family, and packed his knapsack.

Headed east in the rain, he gazed out the window, musing over what had happened. He had to turn in the Zouave outfit. The Commissary Sergeant, a fellow his age named Sam Tanner, leaned on the counter and laughed when he said he was sorry he'd never have the chance to wear the uniform.

"Hobart, the Forty-Fourth is Zouave – most of the new ones are. You're only swapping one get up for another." A second clerk suggested that Hobart turn in his standard issue uniform, too. Tanner intervened.

"Look here," he said. "Walker is transferring from one New York regiment to another. Why take it away when someone will give it back to him in a week?"

A third clerk joined the discussion, insisting that they must follow regulations.

Sam slapped Hobart on the shoulder.

"Go on, before they figure this out. Go rout the Secesh. Maybe the Forty-Fourth needs a Commissary Sergeant. Could be I'll see you in the field."

Hobart nodded, smiled and slipped out the door.

There was a little murmured conversation, but the boys tried to get comfortable on the horsehair-covered seats and slept as they could. The storm followed them across the state, and began to let up as they slowed, arriving at Albany.

The cars groaned to a stop, they got up, stretched and, clutching their valises, stepped with stiff legs onto the platform. Uniformed soldiers, with the inverted chevrons of sergeants and corporals, stood there, bellowing.

"All right, you boys, line up here! Be quick, we haven't got the day to spend! Line up! Line up!" Spotting the occasional uniform in the mass of men, they singled them out.

"You! Private! Over here! You lot make up the first two ranks and try to keep these children in line! Move smart, now!"

The veterans grinned at each other, and lined the others up four abreast, spacing themselves as they had been trained.

When the mass had been herded into something like order, the sergeants led them out, over the rain-slicked streets. They meandered through the morning mist to the Stanwix Hotel. The sergeants hurried them through breakfast, then marched them to City Hall.

"Halt!"

They stood in line for an hour until a man in a resplendent uniform stepped out on the steps of City Hall. Hands on his hips, he looked out over the mass of young men.

"I am Major Stephen Stryker. I am the Commanding Officer of the Forty-Fourth New York Volunteer Infantry Regiment."

Stryker? Related to Mayor Stryker? Wouldn't surprise me.

He added a few words of welcome that none of them remembered, then ordered the sergeants to take over and the long line moved on. Down to New Scotland Road they marched, turned and arrived at their new home – the barracks.

The garrison awaiting them was a three-story, red brick building. A voice from deep within the assembly grumbled –

"Huh! This ain't a barracks, it's a school. We going to school?" A sergeant turned and glared but said nothing.

Another man in uniform, a young Lieutenant, stood before them.

"Our barracks is divided into three sections. There are officer's quarters which are off-limits to enlisted soldiers, the quartermaster storage rooms, and down in the basement, the mess hall."

He gestured at a row of small wooden buildings, the wood still raw and white, that stood in lines next to the taller, brick building.

"These are your quarters. You will be assigned spaces by company, and you are responsible for keeping them clean – all the time!" Hobart rolled his eyes – nothing had changed.

With that, the sergeants took over and began calling out names, assigning the men to various companies. Hobart knew that the standard regiment was made of ten companies and had a total of between 800 and 1000 men. Looking at the formation outside the barracks, he was sure there weren't close to that many lined up. A burly man walked to the front of the formation and faced them.

"I'm First Sergeant Fox! These men will be with me in Company A. Now, listen!"

The men strained to hear. He took a deep breath and began –

"Conger! Cunningham! Cadro! Doane! Ferrand! Gifford! Goodrich! Hooper! Hunt! Knowlton! Parker! Rosborough! Steel! Storm! Van Brechlin! Grannis! Johnson! Nash! Walker! Caddeson! Tanner!

Tanner? Did he just say Tanner? Sam's here?

Risking the fury of the Sergeant, Hobart peeked back over his shoulder. He hadn't seen Sam on the train, but there he was, in the back row. He beamed.

Hobart faced front again. The Sergeant was still bellowing.

"… into the barracks! The first building – right there! Now, move!"

Part of the formation broke ranks and ran into the building. It smelled of pine. There were a number of bunks, but it didn't look as if there were a hundred.

"Fifty. There's fifty bunks. Guess we're going to double up."

Looking around the room, Hobart counted twenty-one heads.

Mighty small company.

First Sergeant Fox seemed to read his mind.

"There's more coming, so don't fret. We'll be at full strength before we go south. Now, get yourselves a bunk and be ready for parade in three minutes. Move!"

There was a disordered melee while they pushed past each other, throwing their luggage onto beds. Another rush as they scrambled back through the door and outside. All around them they saw similar chaos, Sergeants shouting, bodies running and pushing.

Not much like Fort Porter.

That evening, as it began to get quiet in the barracks, Hobart realized that he hadn't said anything to his parents about this new change. He took out pen and paper and wrote.

Barracks, August 8, 1861

My Dear Parents,

I suppose you have heard ere this of the course I have taken in regard to this war, and I have no doubt you are waiting anxiously to hear from me. Well, my dear parents, I am now actually gone for a soldier. I joined the "Ellsworth Regiment" and left Buffalo for Albany last night at 10. 53 – and arrived here at 8. 45 this morning. We have gone into Barracks, where we shall stay until sometime in September when we leave for the seat of war. We are to be well drilled and have good officers and a better lot of men I never saw together. They are not the scum of the city & country, but good picked men, and a great many of them country boys with good old honest country hearts and altogether we will have one of the best regiments that ever went out of the state of New York.

Now, my dear parents, I know that it goes hard to give up an eldest son, but recollect it is in a good cause. I expect to see very, very hard times before I can ever get out of this and so please do not make it harder by unnecessary scoldings in your next letter. I know as well as you that I am a wicked, ungrateful son, etc., but it is too late now.

When we go south we go by the way of New York & I will get a furlough and stop a day or two to see you, & until then I remain as ever your loving, though may be army son,

Hobart M. Walker

Write immediately please & direct "People's Ellsworth Regiment".

I will write every week at least. I have a friend who came with me from Buffalo named Sam Tanner, who is a particular friend of Libbie Tallmadge's and we both brought our bibles & Prayer books. We shall use them & have agreed not to use liquor or profane language and not to gamble while we are gone. May God help us to keep them.

* * *

Buffalo, New York. Sunday, September 9, 1860

It was a mild, pleasant morning and, as they had on other Sundays, the Walkers sat in their pew at Saint Paul's. Hobart was listening, enjoying the mid-service choral anthem while the offertory was being conducted, when he realized that the collection plate was being proffered by someone sitting in the pew directly before him. The hand that held the bronze basin was clad in a white lace glove and the face behind it looked at him, head tilted to one side. Embarrassed, he took the plate, dropped a few coins into it, and passed it along to Stephen, beside him. For the rest of the service he gazed at the back of the woman sitting before him. After the benediction, everyone stood as the clergy, attendants and choir recessed to the words of *Love Divine, All Loves Excelling*. Dr. Shelton intoned the words of the dismissal, and the congregation began to file out. As the people in the pew before him turned to leave, he got a better look at her. Young, he thought, probably in her late teens. Dark hair, tucked neatly beneath a bonnet of the same white lace as her gloves. She was, he thought, very attractive.

As she left the pew, she looked directly at him.

"You sing very well, sir. Perhaps you should be in the choir."

Caught off guard, he stammered. "You're very kind, Miss … Miss …"

"Williams" she replied, "Clara Williams."

"So very pleased to meet you, Miss Williams. My name is Hobart Walker."

"Pleased to meet you as well, Mr. Walker. May I introduce my mother, Mrs. Williams?"

Hobart bowed slightly. "A pleasure, Mrs. Williams."

Brief smiles and the women left. His eyes followed them until they were lost in the crowd. He felt a nudge and turned. His cousin Stephen was grinning at him

"Shall we leave, Mr. Walker, or perchance we could spend the day here?"

On the carriage ride home, Hobart peppered him with questions.

"Do you know her? What can you tell me about her?"

Stephen leaned back and laughed aloud.

"Slowly, cousin, slowly! I may have seen her once or twice, but I did not know her name until she spoke it to you. Find her appealing, do you?"

"No, it's just, I … well, perhaps, but only … "

He searched but couldn't find the words.

"Ah," said Stephen. "The age-old mystery, is it? I believe you may have truly been smitten, Hobart. Cherchez la femme, is it?"

"No, not at all! I just …" he paused, then grinned. "Peut-être … cherchez la femme!"

*　　*　　*

The next morning – early the next morning – a smirking sergeant tore the new soldiers from their sleep, beating an irritating, ragged clatter on an old iron triangle. Someone groaned. "It's six o'clock!" Their training as Ellsworth's Avengers had begun.

Over several weeks, more men arrived and Company A grew larger. Training was relentless. Up before dawn, formation, breakfast and onto the parade field. Every morning, every afternoon they marched and maneuvered. It was much like the days of the Seventy-Fourth, but Hobart knew the drills. The new men stumbled through them much as he had, but gradually the company began to come together.

At noon training paused. Companies marched to the brick building and filed into the basement, standing beside long, rude tables.

"Uncover, seats!" They bared their heads and sat at long, rude tables. Orderlies wove through the room, delivering a tin plate to each trooper.

"What do you have?"

"A piece of meat … I think. A potato. Bread. You?"

"Bread. A potato. A piece of meat."

"Really? Care to swap?"

He paused. "All right."

Solemnly they exchanged plates.

In the evening, once they had been released from the day's drill, the young troopers sat around the barracks. Unlike units like the Seventy-Fourth, where most of the men were from Buffalo and many knew each other, the Forty-Fourth was drawn from all over the state.

"What's your name? Where you from?"

"I'm Charles Gaskell – from Penn Yan."

"Orlando Horton – I'm from Delhi."

"John Robbins – Watertown."

And on it went. There were men from all over the state, and from many different backgrounds. Hobart met young men from towns he'd never heard of, and the evenings were full of tales, boxing matches and even songs. During the day they trained.

September. Summer grudgingly left, and Autumn – blessed, temperate, cooler Autumn arrived in triumph.

First Sergeant Fox moved through the barracks.

"Got most of your men, Sergeant?"

"I believe so, First Sarn't. We got 'em two to a bunk, now. Eighty-five, at muster this morning."

"Very well. We'll have 'em on the field this afternoon. Company drill."

They drilled, they marched, they fired their muskets. After supper, when the lantern lights flickered, there was always someone reading one of the newspapers. Stephen Walker sent Hobart the "Gazette" from Buffalo and his father sent him the "Daily Eagle" from Brooklyn. He became the unofficial source of news for Company A.

"What's on the page today?" They gathered around, and Hobart shook out the pages and scanned them.

"Let me see … why, they have Antwerp raspberries at Arnold and Young's on Fulton Street. Cheap, they say."

"What are you talking about? That's no kind of news!" A chorus of voices from around the room.

"Honor bright, that's just what it has here. Wait, there's more! Says here there's a 13th Regiment fatigue uniform for sale. Only worn but a few times!"

"To hell with the 13th Regiment! Read the real news!"

"Says here the Association of the 14th Regiment will assist the families of those killed or disabled to get their pensions and bounties from Congress. Signed by Colonel Jesse C. Smith, so you can be assured it is accurate."

"Who the hell is Jesse C. Smith, anyway?" One voice boomed from the shadows.

Hobart looked up. "My uncle, to be precise." It was silent, then his friend Sam spoke up.

"Come on, boys, he's just ragging you. Read on, Hobart."

"All right, all right … another flag of truce from Fortress Monroe… Exasperation of the rebels…" He scanned the columns below.

"Wait, here's one you'll like – 'The Rumored Death of Jefferson Davis."

The group erupted.

"Dead? I hope so! That rascal! Is the war over?" He waited until the hubbub subsided, then continued.

"The rumors of the death of the great leader of the Southern rebellion multiply to that extent that there is a high degree of probability of its truth." His eyes flitted down the page. His hands, holding the newspaper, dropped to his lap.

"Sorry, it's Madame Rumor again. Doesn't look like it's true."

The group broke up, most of them heading for their bunks. Hobart and Sam sat together while the lantern burned lower.

"What say you, Sam? Do you think we'll get out of Albany in time to do anything?"

"Couldn't say, but I think there might be something coming. We are receiving more uniforms than we ever have, and the regiment's near full staffed. I was told we'd need to make room for several barrels of crackers in the next few days. Don't know if that means anything, but it is new."

Hobart shook his head. "I think we're near ready. The drill is good, the shooting is getting better all the time. If we don't move before too much longer, I'm fearing we'll stay the winter in Albany."

Sam nodded. "If I hear anything, I will tell you. Good night, Hobart."

Several days later, Hobart was called to the tent of Captain Chapin, the Company Commander. He entered, standing at attention.

"Stand easy, Walker. The Regiment is reorganizing, and they're moving some of the men around. You are one of them – you are transferred to Company I, so pack up your traps and move over to their barracks."

Hobart, surprised, stammered.

"Was there something wrong?"

"Oh, not at all, this isn't disciplinary. I think they want to spread some of the more seasoned men throughout the companies, and you have several months service over many of the others. No, don't be concerned, you did nothing wrong."

He saluted and left the tent. Bundling up his clothing and equipment, he walked down the company street, slippery with September mire, to the huts where Company I had their billets. He entered and several heads, bent over boots and rifles, looked up.

"I'm Hobart Walker," he said. "I've been transferred from Company A."

He was one of many transfers. There were some complaints, and more than one sigh of relief, but for the most part they accepted it. Army life. Two weeks later, the company was called together.

"We need to choose officers, sergeants and corporals. We might be moving out before too long, and the regiment wants leadership in place. Take a slip of paper."

Heads bent low, pencils scribbling, Company I wrote the names of men they wanted to lead them into battle. Some of the men sat, staring at the paper. Hobart looked at the soldier sitting next to him. The lad held his pencil awkwardly and made no effort to write.

"Can I help?" Hobart asked in a low voice.

"Can't write. Never could. Didn't have to, on the farm."

Hobart slid over. "Here, give me your pencil. You tell me who you want, and I'll write them for you." The boy smiled his thanks.

That evening, they gathered around as the darkness fell and the brass lanterns sparkled. A young man, wearing a Lieutenant's bars, entered.

"I am Lieutenant Knox. These are your new officers and non-commissioned officers:

"Webster Shaffer, Captain."

"Edward Spencer and me, Lieutenants"

"William Green, First Sergeant."

"Hobart Walker, Second Sergeant."

He continued reading. Hobart sat back, stunned.

Second Sergeant. Doesn't that beat all!

He settled in to his new role. As the Second Sergeant, he was positioned at the left end of the front rank, that long line of soldiers moving forward. He was the guide, the person on whom all the others aligned. He also assumed greater responsibilities for the twenty privates and corporals who reported to him. He was nineteen years old and had never before had responsibilities as great as these.

"Company, fall in!"

Captain Shaffer's voice echoed across the parade field. The lines of bluecoats moved into position and aligned. They did this without thinking, now.

"Inspection, arms!"

One hundred musket butts struck the ground. Two hundred hands held the weapons upright and still.

"Fix bayonets!"

Long, lethal blades glinted in the morning sunlight. The snap of metal on metal rolled across the field. Shaffer faced Company I and glanced, left to right. Four ranks, twenty-odd soldiers in each rank, looked back at him. Sergeant Walker stood at the left, erect and proud, his gaze steady.

"Men, others in this Regiment have suggested that Company "I" might not be as proficient in the use of the bayonet as others."

A low growl of dissent rolled through the ranks.

"I intend to demonstrate precisely how deadly this company can be!"

An affirmative snarl.

"Upon my command, Company "I" will assume the position for a bayonet charge and surge forward. Your targets will be ... will be ..." He paused and looked around for a suitable mark. Fifty yards behind him scowled a tall wooden fence, pine boards six feet high.

"You will charge that fence and you will destroy it with your bayonets! Is that clear?"

Lusty young voices acknowledged the challenge. One of the Lieutenants stepped up to Captain Shaffer's side and whispered into his ear. He listened, then nodded.

"You will select a suitable knothole in that fence and with your bayonets you will run it through. Think of them as Rebel infantrymen, intent on shattering our beloved Union. Show them how Ellsworth's Avengers fight!"

What was a rumble was now the roar of warriors, blood lust soaring. Shaffer pulled his saber from its scabbard and thrust it high.

"Charge!"

A blue wave swept forward, brave and determined. At a dead run they closed on the snarling enemy fence that stood, daring them to advance.

Hobart thought later that perhaps they might have counted the knotholes before ordering the charge for, by his estimation, there were far more bayonets than targets. Still, his steely eyes fixed on an offending spot, he aimed the point of his bayonet and rushed at it – as did the man to his right and the one beyond him. They arrived at the same knothole simultaneously.

Along the length of the fence, the scene repeated itself, over and over. It was chaos. Comical chaos. When the veil of dust subsided, Hobart glanced around. One private walked past him, his hand held to a bloody cheek. Another lay on the ground. He saw more than one bayonet, snapped in half. The gut-roar of destruction had dissolved into laughter and catcalls. It was, he thought, a thoroughly satisfying charge.

As they untangled, Captain Shaffer walk by. Hobart grinned at the commander.

"Well done, I think, sir, don't you?"

"Yes, indeed, Sergeant Walker, yes indeed."

"Will we try this again, Captain?"

"Ah … I don't believe so, Sergeant Walker, we have accomplished our mission."

*   *   *

He pulled the rough woolen Army blanket up to his chin. The corn stalk mattress rustled as he turned over. He shivered in the dim morning light.

Wow! Really chilly this morning!

He stirred and looked out over the barracks room. No one was up yet, and it was still quiet. The bugler had not yet shattered the morning calm, but Hobart knew he would, and soon. As a Sergeant, he should be on his feet when the dreaded notes of Reveille tore through the soldiers' dreams. He swung his feet out of the bunk and stood, wincing a bit. The incessant marching had left a deep lesion between two toes of his right foot, a laceration which had grown longer and deeper. He'd seen the surgeon, and the treatment the army doctor had applied astonished him. As he wrote to his parents

> … (it went) right across the foot and of course the raw flesh exposed, making it very sore. I showed it to the Surgeon and he poured some melted rosin on it. I never had so much pain in my life, but I am a soldier and must learn to live with such things. I shut my mouth and didn't open it til later.

Summer was well and truly gone, and autumn had arrived. Still shivering, he pulled on his trousers and slung the suspenders over his shoulders.

Guess I should wash the other set today. Glad I have two.

As he pulled on heavy woolen socks, the buglers broke into their morning call.

I can't get 'em up, I can't get 'em up, I can't get 'em up this morning!

I can't get 'em up, I can't get 'em up, I can't get 'em up today!

Around him, soldiers tumbled out of their bunks. There was some muffled swearing, as they moved, half-asleep, through the morning ballet. Wash. Dress. Fall out on the parade ground for assembly.

As Hobart emerged from breakfast into the full morning sun, a private ran across the parade field toward him.

"Sergeant Walker! Sergeant Walker! Captain wants all the non-coms!"

He nodded.

Maybe something IS happening. Finally.

Captain Shaffer waved them into his room. He gestured toward the door.

"Pull that shut, will you? Right. Okay, boys, it looks as if we might be moving, at last. The Colonel wants everyone to pack up their traps, keep their official gear, and get ready to ship the rest home. Do that this morning. Right after dinner, we'll have Dress Parade on the field. Have everyone look sharp – I think there are bigwigs coming."

"Bigwigs, Captain? How big?"

"Someone said the Governor."

The Sergeants looked at each other – this would be something. They left the tent and hurried back to their squads.

Company "I" formed on the field with the rest of the Forty-Fourth, and were astonished to see a crowd of civilians on the far side of the field.

"Must be a thousand out there."

"More'n that – two, mebbe three. I've never seen such a mob."

The Regimental Commander, promoted to full Colonel, strode to the front of the assembly. Hands clasped behind him, his eyes swept over the rows of soldiers standing there. Each held their musket before them, the butt on the ground.

As he did, several horse-drawn carriages, gleaming black, gilt trim glittering, pulled on to the field, and a number of top-hatted men stepped down. As they did, the civilians gathered there burst into a spontaneous cheer.

"That's him! That's Morgan – the Governor!"

Hobart turned his head and said in a low voice "Quiet! Silence in the ranks!"

"But Sergeant, it's him!"

Men craned their necks to look. They could see a man, sideburns down to the points of his up-turned collar, shaking hands with people who crowded in around him.

"Regiment! Atten – tion!"

The men stiffened – backs straight, heads up, eyes front.

"Pass in review!"

The Regimental Band broke into "Ellsworth's Avengers" and the companies marched out. Down to the end of the parade field, then a sharp "Column Left" and another, and the long blue line passed before Governor Morgan and his party. The Governor took off his top hat and waved it as they passed.

The following day, Colonel Stryker ordered another formation.

"Boys," he announced, "I will now give you the program. There will be a series of six-hour leaves, so by the end of the week you all will have had a period to relax and visit your loved ones. On Sunday there will be church services for the Regiment and our final dress parade that evening."

He paused, and the men leaned forward.

"Monday morning, we break camp – we're headed for New York City, then Washington and whatever may lay beyond."

The men cheered. Hobart joined in the huzza, but his face was solemn. He read the newspapers. He knew what "lay beyond."

Confederate General Joe Johnston and the Army of Northern Virginia.

*   *   *

Up before the buglers, Hobart roused the men of his squad on the bright, cold Monday morning. The sun cast a pale lemon gleam across a sky so bright blue it hurt to look at it. Standing on the parade field, Hobart looked around him, taking in the sight.

Might be a good long while before I get back here.

He saw the intense colors of fall painting the hills with fire, and the cold, hard frost where the hilltops lay bare. He saw the Hudson, in the distance, like a gleaming sword blade tossed to the ground.

All around him, troops were gathering up the last of their gear, stuffing their knapsacks full and falling into formation. There was a low rumble of conversation as these excited young voices chattered on.

"Where we headed?"

"I heard Washington, the capital."

"Nah, that's just a stop. We're on for Virginia!"

"We'll probably go right to Richmond, arrest Jeff Davis and be home for Christmas!"

Hobart smiled to himself at that last remark. He wasn't certain how long they would be gone, but he was pretty sure it would be more than a few weeks. Still, one couldn't be sure.

"Company … Fall in!"

Conversation stopped. Colonel Stryker paced along the fronts of the companies, taking the salutes of the Captains. He got to the center and pivoted to face the men.

"Today, we march!"

"Hurrah! Hurrah! Hurrah!" The noise burst forth from a thousand throats.

"Before we march out, there are some things I have to tell you. I spoke to the Governor himself yesterday, and he told me that he could not stand to see his 'pet regiment' – he called the Forty-Fourth his 'pet regiment' …"

Hurrah! Hurrah!

"… couldn't stand to see it march forth without being fully equipped. He has ordered – personally ordered – one thousand new shirts to be added to your issue!"

Hurrah! Hurrah! That's right! Hurrah!

"But that's not all! He has also ordered one thousand new Springfield rifles be sent to us!"

Hurrah! We'll show the Rebs!

"Let us, then, take these good things and march! On to Richmond!"

Richmond! On to Richmond!

A stream of blue poured out through the barracks gate and east, toward the Hudson. Passing through a gauntlet of New Yorkers, wild with delight and pride. Their cheers echoed through the Albany streets.

Midway to the landing, the regiment halted.

"Regiment! Left, Face!"

As one, they turned, facing an ornate residence. A handsome woman, with two small boys beside her, came out through the huge, carved wooden door, a fabric bundle over her arm.

"Present, Arms" Colonel Stryker swept the butt of his sword in a sweeping arc to his lips and dropped his arm, the blade extended before him. The woman stepped to the edge of the porch.

"My brave, brave boys of the Forty-Fourth New York! I am Mrs. Erastus Corning. My husband, formerly Congressman from this district, was influential in the establishment of this regiment, honoring the memory of the gallant Colonel Ellsworth. He knows that you, fine brave sons of New York, will be courageous and bold on the field of battle. He asks I present you with these colors."

She extended her arm and an American flag unfolded. The boys each took a corner and ran down the front steps of the house, extending it before her. Thirteen stripes, red and white. A bold blue union, thirty-six clean white stars. Colonel Stryker swept his sword skyward.

"Three cheers for the colors! Three cheers for Madam Corning!"

Hurrah! Hurrah! Hurrah!

She bowed her thanks, a deep curtsey from the porch, then raised her hand.

"Mr. Corning also asks me to tell you this – he knows not when the government in Washington will be able to pay you, and he wishes to ensure you be paid before you leave Albany. Therefore, he has advanced the sum of twenty-thousand dollars, of his funds, to cover this cost."

The colonel did not have to ask for three cheers. All the companies erupted in an endless roar. Kepis flew in the air and even the civilians lining the streets joined in. It took Hobart and the other Sergeants a long time to restore order and align the soldiers. At last, the regiment moved on. The Hudson, and their steamers, were waiting.

$$* \quad * \quad *$$

The next morning, their steamers arrived in New York City, and the regiment disembarked, marching a short distance to City Hall Park.

"Sergeants, take charge of your men. We'll be here overnight and continue on tomorrow."

After seeing the men of the Company to their billets, Hobart spied a young boy, barefoot despite the cool weather, watching the soldiers. His eyes were bright and excited. Hobart motioned him over.

"Boy, do you know the store of Mr. A. T. Stewart, not far from here?"

"I should say I do! It's a huckleberry over any persimmon on Broadway!"

"Take this note up there, and ask they give it to Mr. Walker. Will you do that?"

"Yes, sir! I'll be off directly."

"Thank you, lad. Here's a coin for you."

27

He turned back to his troops. For an hour, he busied himself in the billets. When he was satisfied with what he saw, he left, walking to Broadway and looking north. At last, he saw a familiar figure walking toward him. A lump grew in his throat.

Father met son and they embraced without words on New York's famous street. Drawing back, Ferdinand looked into Hobart's eyes.

"You're well, son?"

"Yes, I am, Father, well, indeed."

Ferdinand nodded. He looked intently at the young man that stood in front of him, erect and proud. Hobart was smiling, but it wasn't the smile of an impish schoolboy. That boy was gone, and in his place was a wiry, tanned, confident man. For a moment Ferdinand seemed to be searching for something to say. His son broke the awkward silence.

"Mother, she is well, too?"

Ferdinand nodded.

"And Jerome, and George, and Emma?"

"All well, son, all well. They send you their love, and prayers for your safety."

The two withdrew to an adjacent bench, sitting there as the sun dropped low over New Jersey to the west. They talked of Buffalo, and the camp. They talked of Stephen, the relatives there, and the selection to the Forty-Fourth. At last, Ferdinand stood.

"You'll take good care, now, won't you, son?"

"I will, Father, I surely will."

"And you'll write? Often? Your mother will worry."

"I know she will. I'll write as often as I can."

"Well, then," said his father, "I will bid you farewell. God be with you always, son."

Hobart nodded, the lump large in his throat. He bowed his head. When he looked up, his father was gone.

*   *   *

The following morning, things moved quickly. The regiment formed again and marched down Broadway, behind the regimental band, headed toward the Jersey ferry and the trains that would take them to Washington. As in Albany, crowds lined the streets and cheered.

Hobart, at the end of rank, glanced to the east, across the river. There was Brooklyn, saying its farewell. As he saw the familiar heights of Washington Park, rising high above the masts of ships moored in the Navy Yard, he remembered the first time he'd climbed that hill.

*   *   *

Washington Park, Saturday, June 21, 1848

Summer had dawned on Brooklyn, summer with a vengeance. The wind came in from the southeast and he felt it on his back, as he pushed his chubby legs to climb the hill in front of him. His father and sister were several steps ahead, but he pressed grimly on, determined to reach the top on his own. Although early in the day, sweat glued his shirt to his back. He struggled but kept moving forward and up.

When, at last, he stood at the top, he looked around and gasped out loud.

"Father! You can see everything!"

From the crown of the hill at Washington Park, the vista in the eyes of a six-year-old was beyond spectacular. There was no end, or so it seemed, to the wonders that lay before him. He spun in a full circle and laughed. To the east he saw Long Island, farmland and fisheries stretching into the distance and the Atlantic Ocean. He saw the Hudson, stretching its burnished silver arm north until it faded into the purple hills beyond. South squatted Staten Island. Saving the best for last, he looked across the river, to where New York City sprawled, and New Jersey beckoned. He was Columbus, and he had planted his flag in the sandy beach of India!

*   *   *

Washington Park, Wednesday, July 18, 1860

A herring gull, white and gray, wove erratic patterns in the summer currents over Washington Park. On his back, hands folded behind his head and jacket tossed aside, Hobart watched as the bird wove aimlessly about. The sun slid slowly toward the horizon in the west.

I'm like you, bird, ready to fly. Just don't know where.

He sat up abruptly and the bird swooped away, toward the East River and Manhattan. Hobart watched it for a moment. He stood and brushed the grass from his trousers. In a slow pirouette, he looked out over his city.

Below, he heard the bells of Brooklyn's churches peal. He pulled the gold watch, his graduation gift, from his pocket.

Six! If I run I can meet Father!

Chapter 3

Hall's Hill, Virginia, Winter, 1861

It was mid-day, gloomy, cold and wet. Hobart pushed back the flap to his tent and ducked in, shaking the rain off his kepi. Even with a candle burning the tent was dark and it took a moment for his eyes to adjust.

"Hello, Hoadley," he said.

The other soldier grunted but didn't look up. Hobart grinned. With a flourish, he threw back his greatcoat. "Et, voila!"

This time Hoadley looked up. This time he smiled.

"Peaches? You got peaches?"

Hobart extended the can he held. "Only the best for a Corporal in Ellsworth's Avengers!"

Hoadley G. Hosford, of Ashland, New York shared a tent with Hobart. For the most part, he went about his duties without calling attention to himself. While others spent their off-duty hours in games and horseplay, Hoadley read, or wrote in his diary. What did make him smile was fruit, and particularly peaches. Hoadley loved peaches.

"Where'd you find them?"

"Now, you know better than to question your Sergeant, don't you, soldier?"

Hobart took off his sodden overcoat, threw it in the corner of the tent and sat down on his blankets, rubbing his hands against the chill.

Hoadley caressed the can and tucked it away in his knapsack. He returned to his book.

"What are you reading?"

He looked up. "Says here that Virginia gets forty inches of rain each year. Says so right here in the 'Farmer's Almanac."

"Huh. Seems like we've gotten most of that in the past two weeks alone. I wonder if this is ever going to end."

When the Forty-Fourth arrived in Virginia, they were sent to Hall's Hill, where General McClellan had set up quarters for the Army of the Potomac. Each regiment took their allotted space and established their camp, careful to follow the General's precise directions.

"Line up the tents, boys," directed First Sergeant Green. "Little Mac likes those lines straight and even."

An unseen voice scoffed. "And we always want to give the General what the General wants, don't we?"

Green glanced at Hobart, who shrugged. As long as the soldiers kept moving, he was content. It wasn't insolence, it was soldiers being soldiers.

Once the camps were established, there was not a great deal for the men to do, as they awaited the arrival of more troops. Madam Rumor, always active, said that there would be an offensive in the spring, but that was several months away. For now, the Forty-Fourth New York and all the other regiments would try to keep dry, and they would drill.

An east wind whistled across the open field. Colonel Stryker stood at the long column of soldiers, the companies of the Forty-Fourth aligned. He drew a deep breath.

"Column at full distance, on the right into line of battle!"

Battalion guides scurried into their positions.

"March!"

Across the fields they trudged. Occasionally they would march down the roads, but for the most part it was over the fields, through the mud. Always the mud. Cold, gray rain and ankle-deep mud.

Christmas Day. Never spent a Christmas Day like this. Wonder what they're doing back in Brooklyn?

The New Year came and went, and still more soldiers arrived. The rows of tents sprawled over the Virginia countryside, and the lines of troopers winding over the muddy fields grew longer.

*   *   *

Corporal Hosford pushed aside the tent flap and entered. He was laughing aloud.

"You will not believe what has just happened, Hobart, you will not believe."

"Now you have my attention. First, you are laughing, and then you tell me I won't believe something."

"We set out pickets, just as General Butterfield ordered. Everyone was told the password. We wanted to be ready, in case General Dan came by."

Hobart nodded. Daniel Butterfield had joined the Army as a sergeant, was promoted to colonel, and then general. In addition, he had written the Army field manual, Camp and Outpost Duty for Infantry.

"Oh, yes, indeed. So, what happened?"

"Well, Private McLarin was on guard. Manning his post, doing what he was supposed to do. Then, out of the dark, he sees a figure approaching."

"Yes? And?"

"Well, McLarin comes to port arms and called out 'Halt! Who goes there?' He hears a voice say, "General Butterfield."

"Oh, no! What then?"

"He says 'Approach and give the countersign."

"And?"

"Butterfield didn't know the countersign. He said, 'But I am General Butterfield and wish to pass in on business with Colonel Stryker."

Hobart put his face in his hands.

"McLarin brings his rifle to the ready and says – he really said this – 'It don't make any difference if you are Jesus Christ, you can't pass this post without approaching and giving the countersign.'"

The Corporal fell to his blankets.

"I can't stand this! What happened?"

"What happened? Why, nothing happened! General Butterfield turned and walked away." Hobart shook his head.

The next morning, Captain Shaffer sent a runner to find him.

"Cap'n says for you to find Private McLarin and bring him to his tent."

"Did he say what this was about?"

"Nope, Sergeant Walker, just that he wants to see McLarin."

He entered the tent and stood at attention. Captain Shaffer looked up from some papers on his camp desk and then at the Private.

"Private, did you have an … um … a meeting of some kind with General Butterfield?"

McLarin nodded, saying nothing.

"I'm not certain what this is all about, but I have a note here from General Butterfield. He writes 'tell your sentry that he has done well'. Would you care to explain, Private?"

The private looked at Hobart, who shrugged. He turned back to the Company Commander.

"No, sir. Nothing much happened."

There was a long pause.

"Very well, Private McLarin. Dismissed."

* * *

In his tent, Hobart opened the cover of a new diary and wrote

Thursday, February 13. While we were on Dress Parade, Lieut. Perkins, Ass't. Adj Gen of this Brigade, pulled me out of the ranks and gave me a parcel from home containing ½ dozen handkerchiefs and this book. We had Dress Parade tonight in front of the Colonel's tent. Hamilton Ingalls had his discharge read tonight. He leaves for home to-morrow morning. About 8 O'Clock tonight we received orders to be up by Day Break tomorrow, and have one days rations in our haversacks, ready for a march. Where, I don't know, although I hear it is to drive in the Rebel pickets.

Valentine's Day came, and the Regiment made what was little more than a day's march. They got up early, marched out, arrived at a small town and stopped. They munched on the rations in their haversacks and sat, awaiting for someone to have them do something.

Hoofbeats in the distance. The men tensed and gripped their weapons.

"Easy, boys – nobody's seen Secesh up this way." Sergeant Major Herrendeen passed among the troopers.

The horses drew closer and a voice called out "They're ours!" The men relaxed. A small group of men on horseback approached the soldiers sprawled on the ground. As they passed, Hobart heard one voice say, "There's a General!" He glanced up.

The horsemen rode up. One reined in his mount and, as he did, the others followed. The soldiers on the ground jumped to their feet. The man on horse sat erect in the saddle. He wore a pointed beard, gone gray in the middle, and had sweeping moustaches. The men could see the star of a Brigadier General on his epaulets. He swept off his hat, displaying a balding forehead. He looked down at the soldiers and smiled.

"Stand easy, lads. Sergeant Walker is that you?"

"It is, sir!"

"It's good to see you, Sergeant. My regards to your father!"

"I will, sir. I'm sure he'd return them!"

The General nodded, spurred his horse, and the group rode away. "I" Company gathered around Hobart, buzzing.

"You know a General, Sergeant?"

"Yes, I do. That's General Morell – he is a good friend of my father."

For a few moments there was good-natured kidding. They reformed the formation and continued to Vienna. There they paused, then marched back to camp. Hobart went to his tent, opened his new diary, and wrote -

This morning we got up at 4. 30 and breakfasted immediately and by sunrise were two miles from camp.

We did not know exactly where we were going, but Madam Rumor said to drive in the Rebel pickets. About noon we arrived in Lewinsville where there was a Battle in September. It has only 3 houses in it and would hardly be called a village. Here Gen. Morell & staff passed us. The General recognized me. We went two miles & a half beyond Vienna & came in from the rear. We arrived there about 1 O'Clock and stayed there but a few minutes. When we left for camp where we arrived about 6 P. M.

*　　*　　*

It wasn't a battle – it wasn't even a skirmish, but it was better than sitting in camp, playing cards or writing in a diary. He began to feel that something bigger was afoot.

By March the sun had begun to fight through the winter's gloom, and the men of the Forty-Fourth stirred. This time, they were certain, they would be on the move.

"Loan me your pencil, would you?" Hoadley had his diary open to a fresh page.

"Right here. Keeping track of the excitement?" He peeked over his tent mate's shoulder. Hosford wrote –

> March 9th – Something is up. I think we will take leave of Hall's Hill before long. All is excitement.

The following morning, the camp was abuzz.

"Fall in!" First Sergeant Green bellowed. "Draw five days' rations!"

Five days? That's more than we've drawn in a long time. Maybe we are going somewhere.

All during the day the men ran about. Fall in – then stand down. Fall out for dinner. Fall back in. Supper time. Fall in again. It was unusual, but there was no bugle call for "Lights Out" at 9:00 PM. No "Taps" at 9:30.

"No 'Taps'? That's Butterfield's favorite tune! He wrote it!"

The men knew this was different. Right at midnight, the companies fell in. To everyone's surprise, they began to march. Out of Hall's Hill and over the Virginia countryside, through the dark. Marching throughout the night, there were no bands playing, but the soldiers kept cadence with a running stream of comments.

"Why does General Butterfield hate the Forty-Fourth so much?"

"He doesn't hate the Forty-Fourth, Private Carpenter – he just hates you."

At 10:00 AM they reached Fairfax.

"Fall out! Get some rest, but don't stray too far. We're leaving again, soon."

The men sat down where they were. Some gnawed on the rock-hard crackers from their haversacks, while others leaned back and lit their pipes. Many tucked their knapsacks under their heads and slept. Hobart reached down to his side for his haversack and realized, with a start, that he'd left it hanging on a post in Hal's Hill. Canteen, too.

Well, that is a lesson to me. I won't be gaining weight this march.

An hour later, they were back on their feet.

"Fall in! Check your cartridge boxes – you may need them."

The men stirred. The casual chatter that had punctuated the march was gone. Hobart opened the black leather pouch on his belt and counted – twenty rounds. He flipped open the smaller cap box. Twenty-five. He drummed his fingers on the barrel ring of his bayonet. He licked his lips.

"Forward, march!"

The lines moved forward. They passed through thickets of trees and past two small lakes. They stopped.

"Form skirmish line!"

Captain Shaffer turned.

"Company I – form skirmish line!"

Hobart and the others dashed forward, then spread out, 100 men abreast, in a thin line several hundred yards ahead of the rest of the force. Sweaty hands held muskets at the ready.

"March!"

They approached Centerville, trying hard to be quiet. Reports had said the Confederates had artillery emplacements there, defending the area. Company I would be the first to face them.

The men all knew that skirmishers were expected to attack the cannons head on and overwhelm them. They also knew that many of them would fall in the effort. They advanced.

Then, ahead of them, they saw the Confederate breastworks. They could see the cannon barrels, a menacing array looming over the earthen walls. It was still. An unnerving, ominous silence. Captain Shaffer raised his sabre.

"Charge!"

With a loud shout, the line rushed forward. Trampling new grass underfoot they ran forward, bayonets extended, and reached the base of the earthworks. A roar, and they swept over the top and stopped, eyes wide with amazement.

There were no soldiers. No infantrymen, no artillerymen. In fact, there were no cannons. Logs, shorn of their branches, leaned against the earthworks. If the Confederates had ever been there, they had long-since left. A moment of absolute silence, and the company dissolved in nervous, relieved laughter.

"Gone! They've skedaddled!"

"Couldn't stand the thought of facing the Avengers!"

Shaffer called First Sergeant Green to his side.

"Send a runner back. Tell them the entire camp is empty, and there are no troops here. Now, go!"

With the march to Centreville behind them, the Regiment, along with the others, returned to Fairfax. The tedium of camp life resumed, but everyone sensed changes were soon to come – major changes. A week after their "assault" on Centreville, General McClellan arrived, and held a huge parade. The soldiers, while never fond of parades, liked "Little Mac" and he was always effusive in his complements. Then he left, and the rains returned.

The village of Fairfax was deserted, but the officers were adamant that the men stay out of the houses. There would be no looting, they insisted. Bored, Hobart strolled around the empty homes. He admired the neat gardens, now abandoned. These could be much like the homes in West Seneca, or Butternuts. As he passed one home, he noticed writing on the door. Intrigued, he walked up the path until he was close enough to read, and the words were chilling –

If you go to Bulls Run you will find death for all of you instead of us.

He stared at the door for a long moment, turned his back, and left.

On a rainy Saturday morning, the Brigade formed and marched out.

"Heading to Alexandria!" The word filtered back through the ranks.

Several miles short of the town, they stopped and set up camp. One of the men, a private named Seth Cole, chuckled.

"I know the fellows that were here before us. Eighty-Eighth New York – The Irish Brigade. See that post there? See that thing carved up at the top? That's their shamrock – they always do that."

A derisive snort. "Irish, hey? They certainly did not leave any green behind. Just this infernal, bedamned mud!"

Captain Shaffer sent for Hobart.

"Here's two hundred dollars' worth of checks – need to have them get to the Provost Guard Headquarters. That's in Alexandria, couple of miles that way. Think you can find it?"

"Certainly, Captain. It'd be a nice walk and a chance to get out of camp."

"Right. Here they are – on your way."

Before long he was in Alexandria, and found the Provost office, on the corner of King and South Pitt Street. He entered the building and was directed to a Lieutenant seated behind an ornate desk. Handing him the package, he saluted.

"Sergeant Walker, Forty-Fourth New York, with a package for you, sir."

The man looked up, nodded, and took the parcel. Then he stopped and looked back at Hobart.

"Forty-Fourth New York? Is that what you said?"

Hobart nodded.

"Do you know where you are, Sergeant?"

Mystified, Hobart stammered and said "Alexandria, sir."

"Come with me." He took the Sergeant by the arm and led him to the door. Pointing across the street to a three-story brick building on the corner across from them, he asked –

"Do you see that building? Know what it is?"

Hobart shook his head.

"That's the Marshall House, Sergeant."

Hobart stood motionless and stared at the building. It stood on the corner of the two streets, windows flanking a large front entrance way with two rows of windows above it. A flagpole extended from the roof next to a large brick chimney. An American flag flew in the breeze.

The Marshall House. It all began here.

The officer spoke again – "Now you know, don't you?

He nodded. Not quite a year earlier, he knew, a young Colonel Elmer Ellsworth entered that same hotel, on specific directions from President Lincoln, to take down a Confederate flag that flew from that same pole. He took the flag down and was descending the stairs when the hotel owner, a fierce Secessionist, shot him dead. That death sparked the slogan – "Remember Ellsworth" and from it sprang his regiment – the Forty-Fourth New York Volunteer Infantry – "Ellsworth's Avengers." He left the Provost building and walked across the street.

No one challenged him as he entered the front door. He looked around. Everything was quiet, with just a slight murmur of conversation. He climbed the stairs to the second floor. As he turned to ascend the third flight, a maid stopped him.

"May I help you, sir?"

He shook his head. "Just wanted to go … there." He pointed up.

"I'm sorry, sir, but only hotel guests may go up." She was polite, but she stood between him and the steps. He looked at her for a moment, glanced up the stair case, then turned and descended. Without a word he left the building and walked away, stopping once to look back, fixing the scene in his memory. Then he turned and walked the two miles back to camp. It started raining.

* * *

Hoadley Hosford wrote in his diary –

19th March – It rains like fun and last night I lay in a puddle of
water which had run into the tent during the night.

20th – It is a very unpleasant time. We cannot get enough to eat, and
our camp is all mud, so I have called it Camp Misery.

The next day the sun shone. In a burst of activity, all the regiments packed their gear and, en masse, began another march. This time, though, they were heading east, toward Alexandria and the Potomac River.

"Think we're really leaving this time, Hobart?"

"I do, Hoadley, I truly do. There's nothing left at Hall's Hill but debris, and even the sutlers have cleared out. I don't think we're coming back here."

They left camp about noon and marched to Alexandria. By a little after three, the regiment had boarded the steamer *Wilson Small*. The rest of the Brigade was streaming on to two other steamers, the *Daniel Webster* and the *Georgia*. The three-ship convoy left in midafternoon, soldiers packing each ship from gunwale to gunwale.

The trip from Alexandria to Fort Monroe at the mouth of the Chesapeake Bay was uneventful, save for a poignant moment when the convoy passed Mount Vernon. Soldiers crowded the rail to gaze at the majestic white estate with the red tile roof, perched atop a bluff at the riverside. There was an almost reverential quiet as the ships slipped past. Hobart was leaning on the rail when he became aware of someone moving in alongside him. Glancing over, he saw his friend Sam Tanner also contemplating Washington's home.

"I wonder what he'd think if he knew this was happening," the quartermaster reflected.

"Can't imagine he'd be happy," replied Hobart. "American fighting American? New Yorker shooting at Virginian? This cannot be what he had in mind."

Tanner shook his head and the two were silent as the fleet glided past, headed downstream to the Chesapeake.

Chapter 4

Norfolk Harbor, Virginia, March, 1862

Anchoring at Fort Monroe the next afternoon, the soldiers waited, restless, while the ships unloaded. They crowded the rails, chattering, taking in the activity in the busy harbor. Hobart leaned against the rail, looking across the broad stretch of water. On the far side, he knew, were the Confederate lines. Idly, he wondered if the Forty-Fourth would move that way, against the Secessionist forces. His reverie was interrupted when an excited private raced along the deck to where he and others stood.

"Hey, fellows! Come here! You must see this!". The soldier pointed. "Look! Over there!"

Following this gesture, they saw the outline of a ship – a most unusual ship. Unlike the broad sides and tall masts of all the others crowding the harbor, this strange craft sat low in the water, its deck barely above the surface. An odd, circular turret, looking very much like a cheese box, perched in the center. There it was, the USS "Monitor", fresh from its clash with the Confederate "Virginia".

Hobart couldn't resist a bit of regional conceit. "Ship was built in Brooklyn, you know. Not far from my home. Just one more great thing from New York."

The next day, the regiment left the ship and began the march north. Within a day, they'd reached the small – very small – village curiously named Big Bethel. Shaffer addressed the company.

"Boys, load 'em up and be ready to attack. There's rebel ramparts ahead, and General McClellan means to take them!"

The skirmish line edged forward. This was it, the first real fight, and the New Yorkers tried hard to look casual about it.

"Think they'll stand and fight?"

"Not when they see us, they won't. They'll just run."

Or maybe they won't.

"Look! Cavalry!" A small knot of horseman emerged from behind a copse of trees. The Union men fumbled with their weapons.

"Check your loads! Be ready!"

It's primed. It's cocked. I'm ready.

"First rank – fire!"

Sixteen rifles belched smoke. Sixteen rounds sped toward the enemy.

A few puffs – tiny clouds – speckled the distant cavalry. Rounds whistled overhead.

"They're firing at us!"

"Second rank! Prepare to fire!"

Shaffer raised his sword.

"Hold your fire! They're leaving!"

Ahead of them, the Confederate cavalry wheeled and galloped off, disappearing behind the trees. The ranks erupted in cheers and catcalls.

"That's it! Run, you yellow-bellies!"

Energized (and relieved) the Forty-Fourth and the rest of McClellan's force swept on, over the earthworks and into the abandoned camp.

"Like Centerville, all over! Wonder if they're ever going to stand and fight?"

Tents pitched and sentries posted, they settled in overnight. Hobart wrote in his diary –

> Arrived about dark at Chew Point. Stayed all night – splendid roads. A few shots fired by the secesh and then

they skedaddled. Our troops fired 16 rounds, one gun dismounted by its own action.

They continued on through the end of the month and into April. Although the winter's chill had subsided, the spring rains appeared in full fury, turning roads to muddy troughs, in some cases knee-deep. Cavalry and artillery thrashed in the muck, and the infantry moved slowest of the three, struggling on foot along the almost impassible roads.

Two days of this misery and they reached the outskirts of Yorktown. The Confederates were dug in around the town and the site of the famous Revolutionary War battle. Hobart felt the irony.

"See those little hills over there? I'll bet they were built by Washington's men. I had an ancestor that served with Washington – I wonder if he was here?"

Ellsworth's Avengers were positioned at the far right of the line, near the banks of the York River. For almost two weeks they labored through the nights, building and strengthening their fortifications, and defending them by day, inching ever closer to the Confederate lines. They came within range of the Secessionist's cannon, and shells began to fall.

Solid rounds, exploding shells and lethal sprays of grape shot rained down on the New York soldiers.

"It ain't likely to get you, if you keep your heads down." First Sergeant Green lectured them.

There were some close calls, but no one was seriously hurt. Hobart, Hoadley and others were digging trenches when a Confederate shell exploded not far from where Company "I" was burrowing in. Hobart heard the blast and felt his hat spin from his head. A sudden, sharp pain stung his left arm. Glancing down, he found a tear in the sleeve of his sack coat. He touched it. It was wet and scarlet with blood. His blood.

The surgeon looked at the wound, a cut a couple of inches long, between his shoulder and elbow.

"Not deep at all, Sergeant. Let's get a bandage on that and get you back. Looks like that fragment hit your hat and skittered down. But for your hat, we might be bandaging your face!"

Retrieving his hat from the mud, Hobart found a gash in the leather ridge. He perched it at a jaunty angle on his head.

"This, boys, is a lucky hat. I think I'll keep it."

He tugged that same kepi low over his eyes when, two days later, he, Hosford, McLarin and Campbell left the main camp. Crouching low, they crept up to the skirmish line. In a low voice, he relieved the squad that was in place. As they scrambled back, he and the others spaced themselves apart, behind sparse bushes, their eyes fixed on the Confederate lines, several hundred yards distant. He put his finger to his lips.

Dimly, they could hear sounds ahead. Voices, muffled and indistinct. The clatter of pots. Occasionally a horse whinnied. In the light breeze was the scent of smoke, of cooking, of livestock.

"Pssst! Sergeant Walker!"

"Keep your voice down, McLarin! You want the rebs to hear you? What do you want?"

"Sergeant, I hear tell that sometimes the reb skirmishers will come over. They want to trade things, they say. They have tobacco, we have coffee. What do you say?"

"Private, I cannot … I will not give you permission to trade with the enemy. You know better than to ask."

"But they have good tobacco! I can swap that for all kinds of things in the regiment. C'mon, Sergeant!"

"Private, if I don't see you, I can't turn you in, now, can I? If you get caught, well, you're on your own. You may think you're Butterfield's favorite, but if you get trapped, you'll pay the price. You hear?"

The wily Private, however, was already prone, snaking his way through the brush and grasses into the dangerous expanse between the lines. Hobart shook his head.

As he did, he caught a glimpse of something off to his left. Motioning to Hoadley to cover him, he fell prone and, musket primed and at the ready, crawled toward it. He placed each knee carefully, wary of any noise that might give him away. Any snapping twig, dislodged stone or crackle of dried grass. He crept on, at last within easy musket range. He raised his rifle, sighting down the barrel.

He saw the form of a young man, flat on the ground, with his back to Hobart, facing the Confederate lines. He had a large white square of something and seemed to be writing or sketching on it. With a start, the man, becoming aware of the presence of someone else, spun around.

"Who are you?" whispered Hobart. "What in tarnation are you doing here?"

The youth, laying down a large, square pad of white paper, gulped.

"I'm a war correspondent. Harper's Weekly, in New York."

Hobart knew the newspaper, and he knew it to be anti-slavery and pro-Union in its philosophy. Still, spies and provocateurs were everywhere, and Hobart would take no chances.

"But why are you here? Now?"

The man gestured to his pad. "I'm writing a story for the Weekly, but I send them sketches, too." Hobart crept closer and looked at what the artist was drawing. It was an excellent rendering of the scene that stretched out before them. Had he been a spy, he thought, it was more likely he'd be drawing Federal fortifications. He relaxed a bit.

"Best you draw back for a bit. It could be getting hotter up here." As if to underscore his words, something spun through the branches above them, sending a branch tumbling down to the ground.

"Rebel sharpshooters. I don't think but they'd feel you were a skirmisher and try to put the next round in you. That wouldn't make a good story, would it?"

The fellow grinned.

"Thanks. I believe I'll follow that advice, at least until it gets a bit quieter up here." He held out his hand. "What's your name?"

"Walker," Hobart replied. "Sergeant Walker, Company 'I', Forty-Fourth New York. And you?"

" Homer," he answered. "Winslow Homer, and it's a pleasure to meet you."

"You, as well," Hobart answered. "I'll tell my folks back in Brooklyn to look for your paper. You sketch right well."

The war correspondent turned and, on all fours, scurried away from the front back toward the Union lines.

The sun was setting, barely visible behind the rain clouds, when he returned to the camp. As he arrived, several men rushed by him, carrying something in a blanket. Something heavy and still.

"What's that?" he asked.

A young private looked up at him, his face drawn.

"It's Guernsey, I think. Someone said he was shot."

"I didn't hear any shooting. When did this happen?"

"Just a bit ago. He was on the picket line. Think a skirmisher shot him."

"Bad?"

"Dunno."

Just after breakfast the next day, newly-promoted Lieutenant Herrendeen called the company together.

"Private Guernsey from Company H, was shot while on picket last night. He died in the surgeon's tent."

There was silence in the ranks. This was the first of them to die by a Confederate bullet. Herrendeen continued.

"He'll be buried this afternoon. We'll form the company as an honor guard."

They gathered behind the lines, in three long ranks. Hobart stood in the front rank, gazing at an open pit. Fresh earth was piled beside it, dark and wet. A passing breeze touched him with the scent of the newly turned soil, and he closed his eyes. He had not smelled that odor in a long, long, time, but he knew it well.

*   *   *

Brooklyn, December 29, 1850

A small, somber cortege entered Greenwood Cemetery. It was mild for December, and the scent of earth, dank and damp, hung heavy in the air as a black-clad clergyman spoke. He uttered a benediction no one heard, turned and walked away.

The three eldest Walker children – Ada, Hobart and Jerome - clutched each other's hands and stared at the block of polished stone that bore their family name - Walker.

Ada looked down. In front of the stone, a smaller rectangle of stone sat, embedded in the ground. With the toe of one shoe, she brushed aside some dead leaves that covered it. Carved in the stone was a single name – Melvin. Next to it she saw another, and then another. She knelt and with her fingertips gently swept away fallen leaves. Each stone was similarly engraved with a single name – Eliza – Frances – Jane. She counted six in all. And now there would be another – Eliza, born and died that same year. The children stared at them, silent, the breeze that whispered off the harbor the only sound.

"Come, children." Ferdinand's voice was soft. "We'll be off home, now."

At the Clinton Avenue home, Hobart asked the question, the one tugging at him all the way from the cemetery.

"Father, who are those people with Eliza? I can almost remember Francie, but who are those others? There are so many names!"

Ferdinand looked to Elmira, who bit her lip. "I'll have Caroline make us tea," she said, and left the room.

He sank heavily into his chair, the children at his feet.

"We once lived in another town," he said, "Hamilton. Mother and I moved there just after we were married, and I had a shop. Over time, there and here, we were blessed with six other lovely children. They were so much like you, and we loved them very much. Very much, indeed."

The lamps flickered, and they talked. They talked of Melvin and Eliza Melvina, Frances, Jane, Amelia, Melvina and Eliza Maria – all the Walker children, their sisters and brothers, who rested in Greenwood. It was poignant and sad for them all and the tears flowed. As Ferdinand quietly shared the unhappy history, the children unconsciously edged closer and closer together, until they sat, shoulder touching shoulder, drawing solace and warmth from each other.

Chapter 5

Yorktown, Virginia May 1862

Out on the picket line, Hobart and two privates crouched in the brush, looking north toward the Confederate lines. The morning was quiet, the sun rising into a nearly cloudless sky with just a whisper of a breeze coming in off the river. They chatted in low voices, eyes fixed on Yorktown.

Hobart started in surprise – another man in blue had joined them, unseen. A man Hobart did not know.

"Who in tarnation are you?"

"Private Delevan Harrington, Company C. Fellers call me Chris."

"You could get shot, sneaking up on us like that. What are you doing here? You boys are back in the bivouac."

The boy grinned.

"Came up here to watch the fun. Professor Lowe is getting' ready to take to the skies!"

They looked at him, befuddled.

"Professor Lowe?"

"Yup," he answered, with a smug grin. "He's got himself some big balloons, and he's gonna go flyin' in the skies, lookin' down on the Rebs. See! There he goes now!" He gestured over to his right.

They all watched in amazement as a ball, bigger than anything they'd seen, drifted lazily into the spring sky. Long lines trailed beneath it, and as they watched it climbed higher and higher. Guns from the Confederate lines began to fire.

"Rebs hate those things. They keep trying to shoot 'em, but they haven't got one yet. In a minute it'll be out of range and they'll quit."

On cue, the Rebel guns ceased. The balloon drifted higher.

Craning their necks, the men watched it ascend.

"What can they see from up there?"

"I figger they can see all the way into the Reb camp. Heard tell they could count guns and wagons and horses and everything. Sorta looks like a kite flyin' up there, don't it?"

Hobart nodded. Chris leaned back against a tree and gazed up.

"I recollect flyin' kites from a big hill back home."

"Where's home?" Hobart queried.

"Up outside Syracuse. Folks settled there when they came over from Ireland. So many people from the Auld Sod lived there, workin' on the canal, they called it Tipperary Hill. Great place to go in the spring. Cold, gusty winds … you could fair fly a kite as long as you had string."

The boy sighed, then continued.

"I recall one day a boy came up there with a brand-new kite. Bright red it was, and he was puffed-up proud about it. Most of ours were green paper from the butcher, but not his, no! He had a big, big ball o' string and got that thing so high you could just barely see it." He chuckled.

"He was flyin' it with a big smile on his face when another boy walked up to him, pulled out his pocket knife and cut the string. That big kite just flew away – like some red bird. The other feller was fit to bust."

" 'Whatever in all creation did you that for?' the boy hollered. I thought we was gonna have a brawl up there, but the boy that cut the string just stood his ground."

"Ain't never gonna happen that the blood red of England will fly over the green of Old Ireland atop of Tipperary Hill!' The boys with him all whooped and hollered and the one feller just had to walk away."

He smiled, then arose.

"Well, I'm back to the company. You boys be safe, and have fun with that balloon. "

Hobart leaned back against the tree, watching the orb float high over the lines. The breeze washed over him and the sun was a warm caress.

*   *   *

Washington Park, Brooklyn March , 1854

"Father!" Ada exclaimed. "Must we be here? It is so cold!" She pulled her scarf tighter around her neck and turned, trying to keep the blustery wind off her face.

"Ada's a fraidy-cat! Ada's a fraidy-cat! Afraid she'll lose her bonnet yet!" Hobart and Jerome circled their sister, chanting. She flung her head, majestically dismissing them.

Ferdinand smiled through it all.

"Stand over there behind those pines, dear, and I think you'll find they break the wind. It really isn't a bad day at all!"

High atop Washington Park, the Walkers enjoyed the first hint of spring after a cold, dreary winter. A stiff breeze swept in from New York Harbor, but the sky was a deep blue, with only a few feathers of cloud carelessly scattered about. It was a perfect day to be out of a stuffy house, in the bright sun and clear fresh air. It was also a picture-perfect day for something else.

Ferdinand reached for a paper-wrapped parcel he had carried up the hill. With a flourish he opened it. His children cried in delight "Kites! We have kites!"

He assembled the kite and tossed it into the wind. It climbed high into the blue sky and they cheered. Higher and higher it flew, dipping and then soaring, swimming ever upward, racing toward the sun. When they'd reached the end of the string, it was still visible, tiny in the sky above them. Ferdinand looked around.

"See if you cannot find other string. There should be more here." The trio scrambled around the top of the hill and returned with fistfuls of mismatched cords. They knotted each to the end of the kite string and let it out still further, then settled in on their blanket spread out on the grass. Hobart watched the kite sailing so high, almost out of sight.

I wonder what I could see, up that far? New Jersey? Connecticut?

*   *   *

Later that day, back from the watch on the line, Lieutenant Herrendeen walked through the company encampment. Seeing Hobart, he called to him "Sergeant Walker!"

Hobart stood and saluted.

"Yes, sir!" Going to take some time to get used to calling him "sir"

"Help me gather a squad. We're going on a little stroll."

Together they selected ten of the Avengers and cautiously headed toward their picket lines. "Where are we headed, Sergeant Major ... er, Lieutenant?"

Herrendeen chuckled at the slip.

"The Professor in his balloon thinks he saw something in Yorktown. We're going to take a closer look at Johnny Reb's pickets – make sure everyone is loaded."

Hobart passed that word along the line and there was a muffled clatter as soldiers slid their ramrods into the barrels of their Springfields. Each man listened for the thump that confirmed a Minié bullet was loaded.

At the Union lines, Herrendeen spoke with the picket.

"Lieutenant," said the soldier, "I think maybe they're gone. Haven't heard a sound from over that way for hours, now, and usually you can hear them moving about and horses and such."

The officer nodded. Motioning to the squad, they inched forward, leaving the safety of the Union lines behind and moving deeper into the treacherous stretch that lay like a beast between them and the Confederates, poised to devour anyone who trespassed. Spread out in a long line and pacing with great care, they came up to the line. There was the same threatening silence they'd heard at Centreville. They walked forward, each step watchful and measured.

Bits of cartridge papers, the remains of someone's meal, and spots of tobacco juice lay about. Where were the pickets?

"What do you think, Sergeant?" Lieutenant Herrendeen whispered.

No horses, no voices, nothing. No gray coats, nothing at all.

There was a sudden movement ahead of them, and they froze.

Ambush? The soldiers dropped to a knee, levelling their guns.

A young man walked along the embankment. A young black man, with no one else around. Herrendeen called out.

"You! Come here!"

The boy looked up, startled, and his eyes grew wide at the sight of the line of blue-clad soldiers. Slowly he made his way up to the Federals. He stood, head bowed, eyes on the ground. He was silent.

While the others kept their attention on the buildings of Yorktown ahead of them, the officer questioned him. To his astonishment, he learned that not just the picket line, but all of Yorktown had been evacuated by the Confederate forces. Herrendeen pulled Hobart aside.

"Send the fastest man we have back to the camp. Tell Colonel Stryker that we've reached Yorktown and believe the town to be abandoned by the rebs. Make him run!"

Sergeant Walker nodded and a soldier raced back to the main lines. Shortly, a cavalry squad approached at full gallop, along with Colonel Stryker and several of the company commanders. After taking Herrendeen's report, Stryker sent a horseman tearing back to the camp.

"Strike camp," he said. "Immediately! We'll march in and make sure the graybacks don't come back! Tell Captain Shaffer to form his company and bring them up smartly. Company "I" will have the honor of leading Ellsworth's Avengers into Yorktown. On your way, now!"

The horseman wheeled and dashed back. Herrendeen turned to the young Sergeant from Brooklyn and the two shared a tired grin. Yorktown was theirs.

To the martial airs of Siebert's band, McClellan's forces swaggered into Yorktown, Mrs. Corning's colors leading the procession. They found a horrible surprise. Before leaving, the Confederates planted a number of explosive charges. "Torpedoes", they called them - booby traps for unsuspecting Federals.

Over two days, several soldiers were wounded. One was killed. McClellan ordered that Confederate prisoners be employed to locate and remove the obstacles. Once again, Company "I" was called on. Lieutenant Herrendeen was ordered to take a detail to the rebel prison and bring twenty-five prisoners back with him for the detail. As the line of graybacks filed passed his tent, Hobart looked up, and his eyes opened wide with surprise.

"George! George Carter! Is that you?"

One of the Confederate troopers looked over at him. Disbelief flooded his face.

"Hobart? What are you doing here?"

Before he could answer, Lieutenant Herrendeen came between them, and faced his sergeant.

"Sergeant Walker, do you know this man?"

"I do, sir. Our families are friends in Buffalo. I have no idea why he is here, but I ask leave to speak with him – for just a moment, sir."

Herrendeen turned to Carter.

"Soldier, do I have your word – your parole – that you will not try to escape or to harm my men?"

Carter nodded.

"You do, sir. I will not do anything."

"Very well, then. A few minutes only." He turned back to the column.

The two friends rushed together, clasping begrimed hands in a strong handshake.

"George, what in heaven's name are you doing here in gray?"

"Hobart … I suppose it was like you. My family is Southern – you know that – and it just seemed that it was the right thing."

"Who are you with?" Hobart asked.

"First Tennessee - the Big Falls Regiment – I volunteered. We're sent to defend Richmond."

"And I'm sent to take it. I really didn't expect to face a friend like this." He paused. There was an awkward silence.

"I think you might find that a bigger task than your General McCLellan thinks. There are miles and miles of breastworks around Richmond. The city's near to impregnable, Hobart. If you try, I fear many of your friends won't see Buffalo again."

Again the clumsy silence.

"I do hope you might be wrong, George. I wish you well, though. If I can put in a word for you, I most certainly shall."

"You've always been a good friend, Hobart – I thank you for that."

They shook hands again and Carter turned, rejoining the column of prisoners.

The following day, Hobart saw Herrendeen walking through the camp.

"How are your helpers?" Herrendeen smiled.

"Ah…somewhat reluctant. They don't work with much zeal."

Herrendeen ignored their protests and told them that, even if they died as a result, they would have the satisfaction of taking Union soldiers with them. Clearing the explosives was a laborious job, but it was finished with no one else, blue or gray, hurt in the process.

Corporal Hosford stormed into the tent he and Hobart shared. He was furious.

"Do you believe this? Can you even believe this?" His anger was palpable.

"I know. I know. I just heard from Herrendeen. We are going to stay here while everyone else chases the Secesh up to Williamsburg. Have they forgotten who took this town, in the first place?"

Hosford wasn't finished. "Where is Colonel Stryker? Why isn't he up there arguing with Butterfield?"

Hobart turned to face him. "You haven't heard? The Colonel has gone back to Washington. Madam Rumor says – and this time I think she's right – he went to gather up our Zouave uniforms and bring them back. Madam is also saying that he would rather be there than on the line." He paused. "I shouldn't be saying that – it's a rumor. You'd best not repeat it outside this tent."

"No, I won't. Is there nothing we can do? I don't want to stay here while the rest go on. I wouldn't want to be a garrison force."

"Odd you should say that. Several of the officers have signed a letter – I signed it, too – to General Butterfield. It reminds him we led the way into Yorktown, and it asks that we be allowed to join the rest of the Corps."

"Think it has a chance?"

"I don't know. I don't think it hurts to ask."

The next morning, Butterfield's response came down to the regiment. Colonel Stryker, back from Washington, collected the company commanders to give them their orders. Captain Shaffer called together the Lieutenants and Sergeants and outlined their plan. Hobart and the others sprinted to their squads.

"All right, boys, listen. Get your gear together – light marching order – and draw rations. You'll get three days and sixty rounds of ammunition. Move smartly and get back here. We're moving tomorrow afternoon."

The troops scattered, gossiping among themselves. The combination of three days rations and sixty rounds of ammunition meant, to them, one thing. They were moving into a fight. The following morning, before it was light, reveille sounded and by four they were marching.

Hobart and the rest of Company I squatted by the side of the road and watched as several regiments of infantry and cavalry passed. Hobart noticed an old woman emerge from a building on the other side of the road, inspecting the Northern soldiers with narrowed eyes. He strolled over to her.

"Good morning, ma'am. Might you have some food you might be willing to sell? Milk, perhaps? Some eggs or chicken?"

She shook her head, saying nothing. He smiled and tried again.

"We have coins, ma'am, not paper." She looked at him. He sensed she might be weakening.

"I'll be happy to pay you ten cents for some milk or a few fresh eggs."

She looked at him, suspicious, but still she said nothing. Abruptly, she turned and went into the rude house.

Guess I've offended her. Sad … I meant no harm

As he was turning away, she reappeared, four eggs in her cupped hands.

"I'll take fifteen cents. Coin."

He smiled and reached into his pocket.

"Certainly, mother. Here it is."

She handed him the eggs and he took them carefully. As he did, she stiffened, her gaze locked on the nearby road. Hobart turned to see what had attracted her attention.

Striding along the muddy road from Yorktown north came a Union regiment that Hobart – indeed, most New Yorkers – knew well. The Fifth New York Volunteer Infantry – Duryea's Zouaves. In their flamboyant uniforms, there was no mistaking this regiment of Manhattan youths. Hobart turned back to the woman, still staring as the columns passed.

"Don't be afraid, ma'am, they're soldiers just like us. From New York, too."

She wasn't mollified. "Devils," she spat. "They look purely like devils." She continued to stare as the companies marched past, finally disappearing in the direction of Williamsburg. When the last set of scarlet-clad legs was gone, she turned back to Hobart.

"You have your eggs. Let's see your coin."

He handed over the money and she studied it, then put it in the pocket of her apron.

"Thank you," Hobart said.

She spun without a reply and walked into the house.

*　　*　　*

When the last horse had passed, the infantry fell in behind them and the entire V Corps moved north. By mid-morning, the rain had ceased and a hot sun beat down on them. The combination of heat and the still-soggy ground made the march difficult, and then things got worse.

While most of the Corps continued on, the Forty-Fourth New York was ordered to turn right, and follow the Corps on its flank. Then, ahead of them, they heard the crash of gunfire – artillery and muskets.

"Form – ranks!"

The companies hurried into position. Four ranks deep, they loaded their rifles and awaited the Confederates. They didn't wait long.

With a sudden brutal thunder, the underbrush in front of them exploded. There was no beginning and no end to the sound, it rolled on and on without pause. Here and there Hobart caught a glimpse of a form, dodging from behind a tree or stone, but they vanished as quickly as they had appeared, while all the while the pounding of rifle and cannon fire continued. The rain began falling again.

As the rebel gunners poured their deadly fire into the companies of Union troops, the Federals returned the hail. All that morning, in a driving rain, soldiers fired at each other, and dense clouds of choking smoke hung like thick shrouds over the field.

"I can't see what I'm shooting at!" A frustrated voice called from behind him.

"Aim at the muzzle flashes! Fire at will!" The battle continued until late in the afternoon. Without warning, gunfire from the woods slackened, and the quiet was broken only by the groans of the wounded. Hobart looked around. He was horrified.

On every side, soldiers lay in the mud. Some writhed in pain, some feebly pawed at the ground. Others – too many others – lay still.

"What is this place, anyway?"

"Some Court House, I heard. Hanover, I think."

On this late May day, drenched in rain, the Forty-Fourth New York Volunteer Infantry suffered ninety casualties, soldiers dead or wounded. Lieutenant Herrendeen told Hobart that their battle flag, the one Mrs. Corning had given them that bright October morning, had forty-four bullet holes in it.

"Forty-four bullets for the Forty-Fourth New York." There was no humor in his laugh.

As the light faded, both sides pulled back and the firing became sporadic. When it ceased entirely, Hobart and his shaken comrades were withdrawn from the battle line and stumbled to the rear, exhausted and hungry.

They buried the dead and rested. The Sergeants moved among the men, determining who was in shape to fight, and who should be transferred to a medical facility. Even as they sought respite from the fighting, danger lurked.

The day after the battle, in the midst of still another rain storm, their camp was shaken by an explosion – a big one.

"What was that?"

Hobart jumped to his feet and looked out of the tent. In the rain, he could see a pall of smoke hanging a short distance away, like some ghostly wraith in the forest. He snatched up his musket and ran toward it.

Others ran, too. They converged on the spot where Sergeant Howlett's tent had been. In its place, shreds of canvas remained. Sergeant Major Weber sat on the ground, holding his head in his hands.

Hobart put his hand on his shoulder.

"Sergeant Major! Sergeant Major! Are you all right?"

Weber didn't look up. Hobart shook him again. Slowly, the man lifted his head and looked at the Sergeant. His eyes were blank and unfocused – he looked dazed.

A private standing there was talking to the others.

"A bolt of lighting! I swear to all Heaven, a bolt of lightning hit that tent and it just blew up! A great big bang!" The others helped him to the surgeon's tent. Others covered Sergeant Howlett's body with a rubber blanket. The rain continued falling.

The orderly had just delivered mail and Hobart had retired to his tent, letters from his brother Jerome and from Clara in Buffalo in his hands. Without warning, a single, sharp explosion. He ran from the tent.

"What was that?"

George Sheffield, a young private stood, smoking musket in his hand and a look of total horror on this face. Another trooper lay before him, writhing.

"What in tarnation happened?"

"Sergeant, it was an accident, I swear it was an accident. I didn't mean to do this!" Sheffield's hands shook wildly.

"Get him to the surgeon. Quickly! Move!" Two other soldiers picked up the body of the soldier and moved into the dusk, headed for the medical tent.

"Anyone know who that was?"

"Kenyon, I think. I'm pretty sure it was Kenyon. It don't look good."

With a resigned shake of his head, Hobart returned to his tent.

Two letters lay on his blankets. The first, from Ferdinand, talked about the family, and things that were happening in Brooklyn. He held the second for a long moment – it was from Clara. He tore open the envelope and read it. For the first time in what felt like a very long time, he smiled.

A day later, orders arrived for the Regiment to rejoin V Corps with the rest of General Porter's force. Hobart and his company were detached to the banks of the Chickahominy River. Captain Shaffer called the officers and sergeants together.

"We're guarding the engineers, boys. They'll be laying bridges across the river and we are to be certain the secesh don't interfere. Regular picket positions, doubled up. Let's move. " For three days the soldiers swatted at swarming mosquitoes while the engineers labored with axe and saw.

Hobart and Hoadley had discussed this river and they knew that, during most of the year, it was relatively narrow and not too deep. With the spring rains, though, the river regularly overran its banks and spread out in a floodplain, often a mile wide. The soldiers faced this swamp, and building bridges across the deepest stretches was a lengthy and challenging task. They marveled at the skills of the engineers who seemed to create miracles from nothing. When the bridging was completed, Shaffer assembled the company.

"We're moving up again, boys. Draw five days rations and be ready to march in two hours. " The men looked at each other. They were tired, hungry and knew that the gray army on the other side was large. How large, no one was quite sure, but they knew there were a lot of them.

Moving forward, Company I and the rest of the Forty-Fourth set up positions along the edge of a swamp.

"Anyone know where we are?"

"A swamp."

"I can see that, dunderhead. Does it have a name?"

"I saw the map – Boatswain's Swamp."

"Not a glamorous name for a battle, is it?"

"Maybe not. Now pipe down and dig. "

When the Confederates came, they came in waves. The men of the Forty-Fourth and the other regiments fired and reloaded, fired and reloaded. Faces blackened with powder and lined with fatigue, they fought throughout the day. The sun was beginning to sink in the sky before them when a horseman tore into the area.

"Captain! The rebs have broken the line! They're right behind me! They're going to cut us off!"

Shaffer looked around and made a quick decision.

"Reform on me! Double up!"

The lines fell back into a more compact group, and beyond them Hobart could see the men of Maine and Pennsylvania doing much the same thing. Gunfire ripped into their ranks from three directions, and men began to fall rapidly. Finally Captain Shaffer gave the order none of them wanted to hear.

"Fall back! Fall back!"

Without panic, the men backed out of their positions. They reformed and marched, back over the road they'd travelled only that morning, back to the banks of the Chickahominy. One by one, the regiments passed over the swirling waters. The Forty-Fourth was among the last.

When Hobart and the sergeants had shepherded their men back across the river, they saw groups of men swarm the log bridges, and smelled the acrid stench of coal oil as the engineers drenched the wood. As the last one left, he tossed a torch onto the bridge. In moments they were all blazing. The battle was over.

Hobart was savoring a cup of bitter black coffee when a soldier approached.

"Captain wants all the NCOs at his tent." Hobart dumped out the remainder of the coffee and stood.

"Tell him I'm on my way."

In the tent, the atmosphere was somber. There were many faces missing, and the sergeants knew their companies had suffered severe losses. Shaffer stood.

"The Regiment is trying to work out how many we've lost. Muster your squads and get me an accurate count. Let me know who is missing, who you know is dead, who has been wounded or is ill. There's more to come, and we need a good count."

A Lieutenant spoke up.

"Any idea of how many we're missing, Captain?"

"Can't say for sure – anyone know?

Hobart spoke.

"We're missing Baker, Bender, Lieutenant Gaskill and Becker. Lots wounded. Oh, yeah, I think Captain MacRoberts and maybe Vanderlip, too. I'll get you a good count." The other sergeants nodded.

The next day, they reconvened in Shaffer's tent.

"Here it is, boys. General McClellan has ordered General Porter – and us – to take up positions on a ridge up ahead. The whole Army of the Potomac. The Rebs are coming back for more, and General McClellan wants to set up the army on the river. We're going to protect him."

"Are we in front?" It was the question of everyone's mind. After Hanover Court House, there wasn't much laughter in the Forty-Fourth. They wanted revenge.

"No, we're in reserve on the left. But we'll be ready if they call us. Get your boys together. Draw sixty cartridges. Dismissed."

The day dawned. It was already warm, and grew hotter as the sun rose into the sky. Dust to the north and the ominous rumble of horse hooves, gun carriages and marching men were certain indications that the Confederates were active. They were on the move, and headed for the Union lines. Positioned behind the front lines and the artillery batteries behind them, the Forty-Fourth had time to build fires, make coffee, and wait.

Morning gave way to mid-day, and still there was no gunfire. Everyone was restless. Hobart paced along his rank, checking and re-checking each man's equipment. No one spoke much.

Then, in mid-afternoon, Confederate artillery began their barrage. An hour later, Hobart and his comrades were stunned by a ground-shaking blast. The Federal artillery opened fire on the lines of infantry advancing up the long, open slope before them. Before long, the rattle of musket fire indicated the gray uniforms were within range, and drawing closer. The men stirred.

Wounded men began to filter back, men bloodied and mangled. Surgeons and their aides tried to channel them to trees to the army's left, where makeshift hospital facilities had been set up next to a church parsonage. More limped by, or were carried by their friends. "I" Company tried not to look.

At last they were called. "Fall in!" commanded Captain Shaffer, and the cry was echoed by the other company commanders. Hobart and the other sergeants got their ranks into line, muskets loaded and at the ready.

"Forward!" and the blue lines merged into ranks of four and at a quick pace, moved away from their fires and knapsacks, past the artillery positions, and into the lines.

"Halt!" They stopped. Without thinking, the men stepped through all the movements that had been drilled into them.

"Open ranks!" and they stepped forward and to the side, forming the matrix on instinct.

"Ready!" and sixty-seven Springfield rifles were levelled at the advancing boys from Virginia, Louisiana, North Carolina and Georgia.

"By ranks! Fire!" The rear rank fired, then dropped to reload. As they did, the front rank pulled their triggers. .58 caliber Minié slugs tore through butternut coats, and soldiers fell. Still they came, and for an hour rifles exploded at each other, face to face.

Shaffer roared "Fire at will!" and each infantryman fired as quickly as he could reload his rifle. The carnage was terrible. When it seemed as if the gray lines would not be stopped, the order came down "Fix bayonets!" and they fastened the long, evil blades to their rifles.

"Charge!" and Ellsworth's Avengers, with a wordless roar, rushed at the rebel troops. The gray lines stopped, wavered and then began to fall back. The New Yorkers knelt, loaded and fired.

Suddenly, Captain Shaffer spun around and fell to the ground. He lay motionless, and the men closest to him stared in horror. Then he moved – weakly.

Hobart rushed to his side and just as he got to him, was knocked to the ground with a terrible force. He lay on the ground, gasping to catch his breath. After a moment he gathered himself and tried to stand. There was a rush of sharp pain in his left side and he stumbled.

Looking down, he saw a tear in the blue sack coat. He fumbled with a button and turn it back to see a dark, wet stain spreading along the fabric of shirt and down into his trousers.

"You've been hit!" called one of the privates. Hobart could only grunt in pain. Lieutenant Herrendeen knelt at his side.

"Do you think you could stand?" he asked. Hobart, lips set tight, nodded. With several hands helping, he stood. Glancing at the field, he could see the field of gray retreating back down the slope, although there were gray-clad forms on the ground everywhere. Most of them were still, unmoving.

Shaffer moved a little more and Herrendeen said to Hobart "Can you help him to the hospital?"

"I think so," replied Hobart, through set teeth. At that moment Captain Shaffer stirred and made an effort to rise. With the help of several hands, he stood, shuddered, and put an arm around Hobart's shoulder. Handing his rifle to one of the men, Hobart grasped his arm and together they limped away from the field, toward a thicket of woods behind them and to their left. The forms of a white farmhouse, a church and the parsonage were just visible through the trees, and the two wounded soldiers half-walked, half-stumbled toward them.

Reaching the house, they joined a crowd of soldiers, all with red stains on their uniforms. The medical staff scrambled from one to the other, trying to find the worse among them. Captain Shaffer seemed to improve. He sat, leaning against a wagon wheel, but didn't act as if he were in great pain. After a cursory look, a surgeon had wrapped Hobart's wound in a tight bandage, and the pain seem to ease. He gingerly lowered himself to the ground next to his Captain. Neither man spoke.

As night fell, they heard gunfire slacken, then cease.

"Ten-hut!" A voice echoed out of the gathering dark.

"Stand easy, men." General Butterfield and several officers walked into the dim light of the lanterns. He glanced down.

"Captain Shaffer? Are you badly wounded?"

Shaffer struggled, trying to stand, but the General motioned him to remain.

"I'm not too bad, sir."

Butterfield turned to an officer behind him.

"Get this man into a room. See to it now." The man nodded and they lifted Shaffer gingerly.

He looked around, shook his head and left without another word. The others followed him.

Hobart stood, holding his aching side. Around him soldiers lay on the ground, and the few doctors and orderlies moved among them. One of the surgeons spoke, to no one in particular.

"Darn it, it's raining again. We need to get these men under cover. Get them into that barn over there!"

Hobart struggled to his feet. Two more got up and together they began to carry others into the barn. Finally all the wounded were under cover, and a weak light began to spread through the room. Day was breaking.

There was no sound, no warning, and Hobart did not know why he turned to face the door of the barn.

A tall man, rifle in his hand stood, silhouetted against the dawn. A man in a gray uniform. He looked around and then spoke.

"I'm with the Texas Brigade. You boys have just become my prisoners."

Ferdinand and Elmira Walker (about 1860)

(L to R) Ada Walker, George D. Walker, Emma Walker,
Jerome Walker, Hobart M. Walker (about 1858)

Sergeant Hobart M. Walker, Company "I", 44th
New York Volunteer Infantry ("Ellsworth's
Avengers), 1862. Original oil by Bob Langston

2nd Lieutenant Hobart M. Walker, 12th New York Cavalry, 1863

James River, as seen from Belle Isle, Richmond,
Virginia. Photo by the author

Malvern Hill, site of Union Army lines,
Richmond, Virginia. Photo by the author

"Fireworks From the Heights" – Whitman's Brooklyn, Russell Granger. www.whitmans-brooklyn.org. Used with permission

Hart Island, New York

Cape Fear River at Wilmington, NC. Photo by the author

Chapter 6

Richmond, Virginia. July, 1862

His left side throbbed. Each step on the mud-slick road made him wince, and having to help Captain Shaffer stay upright did not make it any easier. The long line of Union prisoners trudged north from Malvern Hill, heading for Richmond in the distance. He could hear the bells ringing, their jubilation muffled by the steady rain that had fallen for the last two days.

"You doing all right, Captain Shaffer?"

The officer grunted, but kept walking.

Along each side of the unsteady column walked Confederate soldiers, guarding the Federal captives. For the most part, they pulled their collars up against the downpour, but occasionally couldn't resist aggravating the Yankees.

"Looks like 'Little Napoleon' ain't comin' to Richmond, does it, Yank?"

"I hear tell McClellan wasn't even at Malvern Hill – big general not even on the field?"

I'd heard that, too. Stayed at Harrisonburg, they say.

For a full day they trudged the dirt roads, arriving at last in Richmond. Late in the day, they came to a halt in front of a long, wide, four-story brick building. Just beyond the river flowed past, foam-flecked and rushing.

Still holding his side, Hobart looked up. "Libby and Son, Ship Chandlers and Grocers" the sign read. The first two stories were painted white, the upper two bare brick. A Confederate battle flag flew from a pole in the center of the building.

"Line up! Officers over here! The rest of you – line up over there!" Shaffer squeezed Hobart's shoulder and faltered slowly over to the first line.

A group of gray-clad troopers searched them. His weapon had been left behind on the battlefield, and his leather belt with its cartridge box, cap box and bayonet scabbard were taken by the Texas soldiers that captured him, but he'd picked up a canteen and a knapsack as they left Malvern Hill. A private with bad teeth seemed to take great delight in searching the Union Sergeant. Emptying his pockets, Hobart held his pocketknife and a few coins in his hands. The soldier took the cash, and said with a grin -

"Y'all won't be needin' that – ain't much to buy where you're goin,'" To his surprise, the rebel soldier returned the knife. After a cursory inspection a man who didn't act like a doctor and smelled like a stablehand glanced at the bandaged side and said "You're still standin' – you ain't hurt bad". They were herded into a large empty room.

Empty, except for the hundreds of Union prisoners who milled about. Hobart looked over the room, but gave up trying to estimate how many there were. A guard nudged him.

"That your canteen?"

"Yes, it is."

"Wanna sell it?"

The thought had never occurred to him, but he did some quick calculations. The soldier who had searched him had taken what little money he had, and it crossed his mind that having some money might help.

"I might. How much?"

"I'll give you a dollar and a half."

"Two"

"All right, two." The man handed him two bills and took the canteen. Hobart glanced at the money. Confederate scrip. He had no idea what it might be worth, but he did see other transactions going on around him. A woman outside the window was selling something, and Hobart edged over to see.

"Bread," she was saying to another trooper. "Fresh baked this morning."

The man bought a loaf and moved away. Hobart slid to the window before anyone else could get there.

"What do you have, ma'am?"

"Got bread and some crackers," she answered.

"How much for two loaves and a bag of crackers?"

"Dollar twenty-five."

"I'll take it." He pushed the two bills through a crack in the shutter. She took it and pushed back a coin and a bill. He tucked them in his pocket and moved away. In a corner, he pulled out the coin and the bill and held them in the light. With a wry chuckle, he saw that the bill was ornately printed "Confederate States of America, Fifty cents", the coin was a standard American quarter.

He had just put the money away when he felt a hand on his arm. In the gloom someone spoke.

"Hobart? That you, son?"

He spun around. Looking at him, tired, dirty but still grinning, were several familiar faces.

"George! George Barnard! Good to see you! We thought you might have been killed!"

"Nope, they grabbed me at Gaines Mill."

"Anyone else here?"

"Well, there's George Edmonds, Charley Gaskill and a few others. A few hurts, but mostly all right. How about you?"

"I took a shot at Malvern Hill, but I think I'll be all right. Got some bread here. " He proffered the loaves.

"That's bully! We haven't have hardly anything to eat!"

"Gather the boys – we'll share what we have."

75

They milled around, voices alive with excitement. The bread disappeared in several bites.

Two days later, Hobart awoke, stiff and aching, sweat streaming down his face. The little group of Forty-Fourth New York soldiers had spent part of the previous evening trying to estimate how many men had been packed into the former tobacco warehouse. After a spirited discussion, they came to their conclusion.

"Five thousand? You think there are as many as five thousand soldiers here? That's five regiments, you know!"

Whatever the number, there was something stirring that morning. Men went from group to group, whispering. The guards gripped their weapons, unsure of what might happen. At last, a small knot of men stood up in one corner. The rest of the room stared at them and the cavernous room fell silent. A strong, throaty voice broke the silence.

"Ten-HUT!" The men scrambled to their feet. The guards tensed. The knot in the corner drew a deep breath and began.

"Oh, say, can you see, by the dawn's early light? …" The men of the Forty-Fourth were upright and singing with fervor. Hobart turned to a few standing near him, looking on, silent and uncertain.

"C'mon, boys – it's the Fourth of July!" They snapped erect and joined in.

"Whose broad stripes and bright stars, through the perilous fight …" The Confederate guards looked at each other, at a loss. The soldiers in blue, facing the windows, sang, the sound growing ever louder as more voices joined in.

"O'er the land of the free, and the home of the brave!"

A loud "hurrah!" and then laughter. A few voices broke out in "The Battle Hymn of the Republic", and they sang that, too. Then "John Brown's Body", until most of the room was laughing. The troops in gray relaxed, some even smiling in relief. For a moment, Hobart felt better than he had in weeks, but his euphoria didn't last.

As the laughter faded, he slumped, back against a wall. The room was stifling, the air thick, and his side throbbed, no matter how he shifted. He looked around the room and shook his head. There were so many, many soldiers crowded in that moving around was difficult, almost impossible. The guards looked on, most of them without expression. From time to time he could hear a Southern voice, usually tossing an insult at some captive Federal, but for the most part the only sound was the murmur of many voices, speaking quietly. He shook his head.

Never had a July Fourth like this. Wonder what they're doing in Brooklyn? He leaned back, against the filthy wall. He closed his eyes.

*   *   *

Brooklyn, New York. July 4, 1849

The day atop the hill in Washington Park, was one that stayed in the children's memories for a long time. Ada wiped chicken from Hobart's chin, the boys picked up the remains of their picnic, and Ferdinand drew a slim book from his pocket.

"Children, sit here and I'll read you a tale. A frightening tale … a ghostly tale!"

The three giggled in shivery anticipation and sat, folding their arms around their knees. Ferdinand opened the book and with high drama said – "The Legend of Sleepy Hollow, by Washington Irving". While a rude cluster of seagulls squabbled and chattered overhead, he read. Ichabod Crane … Katrina Van Tassel … Brom Bones and, of course, a fearsome headless rider on horseback. Hobart could not remember a better day.

"…and the plough-boy, loitering homeward of a still summer evening, has often fancied his voice at a distance, chanting a melancholy psalm tune among the tranquil solitudes of Sleepy Hollow."

Ferdinand closed the book with a flourish – Ada and the boys, faces bright with smiles, applauded. "Read another! Yes, one more, Father!" Ferdinand grinned.

"Let us do something better – I'll tell you a story – a true one, this time. You remember Mother and her tales of Grandfather Danielson?" They nodded, eager. "Well, now, it was in June of 1775 – a warm day, much like today. The British forces marched out of Boston to drive the American patriots from their trenches, high on Bunker Hill. And there, in those same trenches, was a young man named Timothy Danielson. Do you know who he was?"

The children had heard this story any number of times, and knew it well, but shook their heads. Ferdinand continued – "He was Mother's grandfather, Timothy. Why, he had been there on Lexington Green when the redcoats marched in. Do you remember the poem? 'By the rude bridge that arched the flood …'" Again, enthusiastic nods.

"And after that, he marched with his neighbors to Boston – to Bunker Hill. " He looked left, then right, then leaned in toward the children. Voice hushed with dramatic conspiracy, he said "It was actually Breed's Hill, but they call it the Battle of Bunker Hill. " The trio tittered, as though they were party to some great secret.

"In the trenches at Bunker Hill, Timothy stood bravely while the redcoats advanced. Then, a musket ball shattered his gun! While he held it!" They shuddered. "So he had to leave the hill, but he was with General Washington right to the end. " He sat back, smiling, while Ada and the boys cheered.

The sun began to set beyond New Jersey to the west. More people gathered atop the hill. The children grew curious and a little restive. After all, it was growing dark and they all knew that meant they should be in bed. Still, Ferdinand showed no inclination of leaving, and he was Father. They were with him and they were safe.

When the sun had vanished beyond the horizon, the sky above Battery Park, below them and across the river on the southern tip of Manhattan Island, was black – black as coal. Then, with no warning, it exploded in fountains of brilliant light and color. Deep, thundering explosions shook the night. It was by far the most glorious thing they'd ever seen, and they gaped in awed silence. Fountain after fountain, rocket upon rocket, boom upon boom the display continued. Then, not to be outdone by their rival across the river, Brooklyn answered back with a display just as magnificent, but more exciting - it came within yards of where the Walkers were sprawled on the ground. It was so close that bits of paper floated over from the shells that had burst overhead. On and on and on they roared and everyone cheered.

When at last it subsided and the final fiery burst dimmed, Ferdinand spoke.

"Come, it is time we were off home." Jerome had fallen asleep and Ferdinand carried him down the slope, but Adaline and Hobart, hand in hand, walked. In the streets, firecrackers popped and burst.

Chapter 7

Libby Prison, Richmond, Virginia. July, 1862

July Fifth dawned as if nothing of any significance had happened the day before. For several days, the men did little more than sit on the hard floor and talk.

The sun had just begun to creep through the dirt-smeared windows when groups of Confederate guards entered the room.

"Hobart! Hobart! Wake up!" With a fierce whisper, Charley Gaskill shook his shoulder.

He sat up and rubbed his eyes.

"What is it? What's happening?"

"Don't know, but there's more of them than we've seen yet. Something is up."

The guards moved about the room, counting off groups of soldiers. They came to where the New York boys sat and, together with fifteen-odd others, pushed them into a group. The Union men looked at each other, uncertain.

A Confederate officer entered the room, looked around, then pointed at the bunch closest to the door. He spoke one word.

"Move!"

One by one, the squads of prisoners were led out of the Libby building. Hobart's group was the third.

Out on the street, the guards lined them into a rough column. The same officer came out of the prison, looked around, and with a gloved hand, motioned to Hobart's group. They began to walk.

They marched north on a road that paralleled the river, then herded up a steep bank to where a ramshackle bridge was anchored to the Richmond shore.

As the line snaked across the trembling footbridge, Hobart looked down at the James River, flowing below. George Barnard walked at his side, and the two spoke softly.

"I think we're headed to that island. " It was one of several islands in the river. The current swirled below.

"Current looks pretty swift. Think you could swim it?"

Barnard shook his head.

"Not me. Never much of a water boy. You?"

Hobart shrugged.

"Maybe. I'd have to think about it.

The island had no walls or fences – he guessed the Confederates thought the river was enough of a barrier.

They could be right.

A swarm of armed guards formed a gauntlet and the Yankee prisoners passed through.

A thought occurred to Hobart - the soldiers he had seen on the battlefields had been like him – almost all young, fit-looking youths. These guards, although armed, were much older, with more than one graybeard among them. There were those whose girth suggested more comfortable living than outdoor combat, and Hobart thought

Second-line troops.

He tucked that thought away.

"Don't think they knew we were coming. Where does everyone go? Where do they sleep?"

One or two rough shacks, some lightweight tents, and a scattering of makeshift shelters bore little likeness to the company streets and straight lines at Hall's Hill.

The group dissolved, soldiers wandering off in all directions. Hobart found himself next to a soldier, arm in a sling, but in a uniform similar to his, a scarlet shirt showing under his sack coat.

"My name's Walker. Forty-Fourth New York. You a Zouave?"

The man, who looked older than many of the callow youths there, nodded.

"John Wust," he said. "Company 'D', Fifth New York."

"Duryea's?"

Again, he nodded. "Yup, none but the best. Caught this," he gestured with the immobilized arm, "at Gaines Mill. Been here a couple days."

The two chatted while the new prisoners milled around. "What can you tell me about this place?" asked Hobart.

Wust motioned with his good arm. "Get away from these fresh fish and I'll tell you what I know. " The two sat on a log and Wust continued.

"You'll want to be careful until you've got it figgered out. There's all kinds here, and some ain't so friendly. Mostly none of us came here with our traps, so nobody has much, but there's those that'll take whatever you have, without so much as a 'by your leave'. There's some hard cases and you'd best stay shy of 'em."

This made sense to Hobart.

"Go on. What else?"

"Well, there don't appear to be too much to fill your bread basket, and Johnny Reb ain't in a hurry to set up a banquet. They bring out some bread in the morning, and it's best to eat some and hide the rest. Set you up a place to rest, shelter from the rain, and you'll be hunky dory."

"How long do you think we could be here?"

"Hard to say," the older man scratched his cheek. "Madame Rumor is sayin' we'll all be paroled soon, and, truth be told, there's been some taken off the island. More come on than go off, but some do leave. Couldn't say for sure. It's right warm now, but I don't think I'd want to be here when the leaves fall."

At that moment the church bells in Richmond, across the foaming rapids to the east, began to chime the hour. Taking his first good look at this view of the city, Hobart saw a hill rising into the sky, above the buildings clustered along the river.

My God! That looks just like Washington Park!

It began to grow dark. There were no tents for them, so he, Barnard, Edmonds, Gaskill and several others found a spot by a slight rise. A cool breeze drifted in off the river, and it was surprisingly comfortable. Just before drifting off to sleep, he thought

Wish I could get a letter to Father – he must be very worried. This place is paradise, though, compared to the prison.

While he slept in the dirt of Belle Isle, in Brooklyn his father had begun to fear for his son. Each day he scanned the newspaper, looking for news.

McClellan's Last Contest with the Enemy

The Enemy Driven Back!

He was encouraged, but still concerned.

Where was Hobart?

When a week had passed and he'd heard nothing, he sat at his desk, pen in hand. Unfamiliar with military ranks or protocol, he wrote to General Fitz John Porter, the Divisional Commander, and one addressed to "Hobart M. Walker or Captain Shaffer of Co "I". He was astonished when, in a week, he opened a letter -

> Headquarters, Morell's Division
> Camp at Harrison's near James River
> Va July 10/62
>
> My dear sir:
>
> I am this moment in receipt of yours of the 8th.
>
> I had a conversation with Lieut Col Rice, who now commands the Forty-Fourth Regt, this morning about your son to use his promotion. Col. Rice said he was missing but was probably a prisoner. As soon as I can learn his fate I will inform you & be assured if I can do

anything to promote his interests I will take great pleasure in it.

The Division formerly under the command of Gen. Porter is now commanded by me. It suffered seriously during late battles.

Very truly,
Your friend
Geo. W. Morell

Ferdinand was heartened.
George Morell, his good friend! Commanding Hobart's Division!
Later, a letter from Lieutenant Herrendeen -

Sergeant Walker was last seen helping an injured man from the field. Should it be that he was made a prisoner we shall doubtless soon hear from him, as exchanges are constantly being made.

The next month Herrendeen wrote again, reporting your son (Sergeant Walker) is a prisoner in Richmond.

*   *   *

July passed without haste, and the summer sun burned down on the marsh grass of Belle Isle. It turned brown and dry, as did the soldiers imprisoned there. Hobart's side continued to heal and to his surprise, it didn't seem to become infected. At first, the prisoners were put to work, erecting tents, but after that, their days ran together, each one the same.
Food. It was always about getting something … anything … to eat.
He still had his diary and began to write each day.
Had some bacon today.
Half a loaf of bread & a small piece of bacon.
Small groups of soldiers were being paroled, but more were arriving, seemingly every day. The mismatched collection of tents strained to hold them.

Hobart and the others welcomed the other private from New York, John Wust, into their circle. Each day they gathered to talk. It was frequently the only thing they had to do.

Late in the month, Wust came by to shake his hand and say -

"I'm to be paroled. Don't know if'n I'll see you again, but keep your powder dry and take care of yourself."

Pulling himself to his feet, Hobart looked him full in the face and said "You, too, John. Maybe we'll meet again." and watched as his friend passed over the bridge to Richmond and out of sight. With him went Edmondson and Barnard. He was beginning to feel alone.

Avoiding, as Wust had suggested, the "hard cases", Hobart survived the summer, his biggest battle fighting tedium.

"Hobart, want to come down to the field? The boys are putting together a game. "

"What are they playing?"

"Quoits, I think. Maybe rounders."

"We can always play Dance with Madame Rumor."

"I'm going to the field. I'll see you later."

"I might go down to the river for a wash."

With just the uniform he was wearing when taken, and the few items he'd found in the knapsack, Hobart tried to keep himself as clean as possible. They were permitted to wash their clothing and even bathe in the James. Always, however, an ominous row of Confederate cannon on a high ridge overlooking the camp and the omnipresent armed guards left no doubt – they were captives.

On a hot, humid morning, he went to the banks of the river to wash out his clothing. Hanging his sack coat on the low branch of a hackberry tree, he took off his shirt, trousers, socks and underdrawers and crouched, naked, at the water's edge, trying hard to remove some of the sweat and dirt that accumulated.

He watched the water flowing by.

Bet I could swim across. No wider than Wallabout Bay, and I've done that. Many times.

He stopped scrubbing his shirt and stared at the river. His reverie was broken by a voice behind him, and he looked up, startled.

"I wouldn't even give it a thought, Yank." Glancing back over his shoulder, he was looking at a prison guard.

The man was tall and slender, his face leathered. His uniform was gray, but bore no insignia and no rank. Instead of a kepi or forage cap his head was covered by a slouch hat – black, greasy and pulled low over his eyes. Long salt-and-pepper hair hung from below the brim and onto his shoulders. His beard was streaked with gray and untrimmed. He cradled a rifle in the crook of his left arm, while his right hand rested on a long-barreled revolver in his belt. On the left side of a brass belt buckle, with the letters "CS", a long, bone-handled knife with a vicious blade hung in his belt. The soldiers called it an "Arkansas Toothpick", and it looked lethal.

He spoke – in a quiet, flat tone – almost monotone.

"You ain't got a chance, even if'n you tried it, Yank. You wouldn't be ten yards into the river and I'd have a ball in the back of your head. I kin knock down a squirrel atop a tall tree, and you're a durn sight bigger than a squirrel. " He spoke without emotion, making it all the more worrying.

Hobart looked at the rifle. Not a Springfield, certainly, and not one of the Enfields that both sides purchased from England. In fact, it wasn't a percussion cap rifle at all, but a flintlock, and it didn't seem at all familiar to him. The man followed his gaze.

"Ain't nothin' no army gives ye. My Pappy got it from his Pappy – made up in Pennsylvania, they said. Carried it since I was a boy. I'm real handy with it." Not a threat, a quiet statement of fact.

He drummed his fingers on the pistol in his belt. "You try it and I might just save a musket ball. I kin get you with this, too. Got it off a fella who come back from the war down to Mexico. I give him a prime pelt and a full gallon of 'shine. It's one of them Colt revolvers, made up North some'ere. A Walker, they call it."

Hobart grimaced at the irony but said nothing.

The man continued "You just finish your duds, there, and don't do nothin' foolish. There's talk you boys might be goin' back soon, anyways. " Spitting a long stream of tobacco juice to the side, he turned on his heel and left. Hobart finished, put on the still-wet clothing and returned to the others.

Another contingent of prisoners arrived. Hobart and several of the Belle Isle veterans gathered together as one of the new arrivals spoke.

"We were taken at Bull Run. Sent us all the way to Salisbury and packed us in like fish. More and more kept coming and didn't seem like anyone knew what to do with us. They weren't mean, just too many of us, I guess. Finally they dragged a bunch of us out and sent us here. I tell you, boys, this is a darn sight better than North Carolina. Be thankful."

There was a flurry of excitement at the river's edge and several of the men rushed over.

"There's a Colonel there! One of ours! Says he wants to talk to us." The group wandered over. Standing there was a tall, slender man in an officer's uniform. When he spoke, there was an unmistakable Irish lilt to his voice.

"Men! I'm Colonel Michael Corcoran, late of the 69th New York, taken at Bull Run and held until now at Salisbury. I'm here to tell you to keep heart, your imprisonment will not last long. There is a regular exchange coming, and I believe that you'll soon be back with your loved ones. Keep heart, boys, and stay strong!" He strode away.

"You think he's right?" A young soldier standing next to Hobart looked at him, pleading in his eyes.

"I don't know. It would be nice, but rumor builds upon rumor here and can't say but what I hardly believe it. We'll have to be patient, I think." The boy seemed disappointed at this and walked off.

The longer the men spent in captivity, the more they wanted to believe anything they heard. A copy of the Philadelphia "Enquirer" passed from hand to hand, eagerly read and passed along. Several troopers who could not read begged for someone to share it. Hobart folded back the pages and scanned the article.

"Says here those prisoners who are well will be exchanged and sent right to their regiments in camp. The sick and the wounded will be sent to the hospital."

"Will we get a furlough?" one asked.

"No, it says here 'without furlough'" They groaned.

As the summer wore on, the food supplies dwindled, and the rumors swirled throughout the island. Hobart felt that, as a Sergeant, he was responsible for keeping matters calm, but sometimes the stories had the ring of truth.

The citizens of Richmond, one said, were tired of feeding Yankee prisoners. They were having great difficulty in feeding themselves, and certainly didn't want to share anything with the hated soldiers in blue.

One morning, a soldier pointed across the river and exclaimed "Look! Look over there!" Heads craned, but no one noticed anything out of the ordinary on the Richmond Shore.

"Can't you see? Look at the building, over there! See that flagpole? The flag's at half-mast! What does that mean? Is it over? Are we going home?"

All day the camped buzzed, with story upon fantastic story spreading through the crowds. Finally, an officer in gray with three gold stripes on each side of his upright collar strode into the camp. He had his hand on a pistol at his belt and his words were bitter and cold.

"I've heard tell you think that General Jackson has died. Well, I'm hear to tell you that ain't truth, not a bit. Next man I hear spreading that rumor will be shot! By me!" With a glance of icy hatred he spun and left.

Late in the afternoon the day's ration was brought to Hobart's squad. Soup and bread. He looked at the scant half-cup and couldn't stop a snort of derision.

"Guess they're upset with us, spreading rumors. Look here – clear bean soup. I see two beans and three flies – that's about the closest we're going to get to meat today. " There was a tired chuckle from the others that faded quickly. That night the breezes off the river, that had kept the camp cool, blew in cold – unmistakably cold.

Rumors again swept the camp. The sergeants did their best to quell them, but when the occasional newspaper made it over the rickety bridge from Richmond, there was fear that the concerns might be grounded. A sergeant from a Vermont regiment came to Hobart's tent.

"Sergeant, I want you to keep this on the quiet, but we're meeting tonight at our tent, right after the sun goes down. Don't make a fuss and don't tell anybody, but you should be there." Hobart nodded.

When they gathered in the tent, the Vermont Sergeant spoke.

"Boys, this could be serious. Seems that General Pope, out there in Arkansas, has been dealing with secesh guerillas harassing his troops. Thinks they're hiding out among the citizens, then sneaking out to attack our boys. He published a notice saying he was going to hold the citizens responsible if it happens again."

A voice from the back of the tent. "What's he mean – 'responsible?' "

"Means he's going to hang someone."

A murmur swept the group. Evidently no one thought this was such a bad idea. The sergeant continued.

"The secesh have said that Washington had better recall Pope, or they're going to take people from the prisons and hang them. I don't know if they mean officers or any soldier, but that's what they said, and we think they mean it. If they do, we need to be ready for it."

"How so, sergeant?"

"Because we're not going to let them do it." His voice was quiet, but rock-steady.

Trying to keep their voices down, the tent buzzed. Hobart stood up.

"Can't speak for everyone, but I will speak for my New York boys. The rebels had better not let us know of it before they are ready to go to work, for it sure will take more than one brigade to guard all of us." There was a low growl of agreement. They were prisoners, but they were still soldiers.

The summer approached its end, the nights grew colder, and it became harder to keep up his spirits. The foot injury that had caused him such pain in Albany began to throb, and the gun shot, while healing, was not completely well. And always there was the pervasive hunger. Diligently, he recorded in his diary

August 24 – bread & water – prisoners fare. Some soup, but very
poor & dirty. Somehow one can't make these Sundays

feel like old-fashioned Sundays. I read considerable
in the Bible today but it doesn't seem natural.

August 26 – Quite sick today – intermittent fever

August 27 – My foot is very lame & I can't stand on it.

August 28 – Foot about the same. Treated it to a bread poultice.
Went without breakfast for the purpose.

August 29 – Foot quite bad, another poultice.

August 30 – I wish I were off this hated island & out of the
hands of the secesh, a freeman once more. No
bird in a cage ever felt it more than I do here.

August 31 – Rumors on rumors multiplied. Going away tomorrow
or this week – certainment. Confound the rumors as
long as I could get away from here. I want to go home.

Each day, the level of excitement rose. Rumors flooded the island,
ebbing back and forth as first one story and then another swirled like
the waters of the James. They would be leaving – they were staying. The
men awoke each morning animated and went to bed deflated. Then, mid-
month, it finally happened.

September 12 - Today commenced to parole all on the Island. Great
excitement rumors of secesh defeat, etc., etc. Hunter &
Buell on the march for Richmond with 200,000 men.
Todays paper gives extracts from northern papers which
say that it is impossible the secesh to cross the Potomac
or go through Kentucky. That vols enough are going
out from Ohio to blacken the hills of Kentucky. I went
out with squad No. 1 Instead ff 11 although am a little
afraid something may turn up. It rains & I thought
it better to take my chances than to get wet through
waiting further. Today papers advertise a deserter 10
years of age, 5 fee 8 inches in height. $150 reward.

September 13 - 6 clerks & tables to work. Busily engaged all
night paroling men but through some mistake (quite
common things in secession) from 19 to 36 have
to be gone over again. Old men & all went over

> to Richmond with the sick. About 10 ½ AM left
> the Island. I went with No. 1 went over to the city,
> passed the Libby Prison, saw Pope's officers. From
> there to Aikens Landing 12 miles hard march.

There, under a fluttering white flag, the column stopped. In front of them was a group of officers in Union blue, and behind them a bedraggled collection of men in gray. An officer from the Richmond group approached the Union officers, saluted and the two spoke, out of earshot of the column. The men stirred. They saluted again and returned to their respective columns. The officer faced Hobart and the others.

"You have been paroled to your own forces. You are free to go. " The group rushed forward to where the Federal men waited. The now-free Confederate soldiers did the same, the two groups ignoring each other as they passed.

Amid handshakes and hugs, they were back among their own. Hobart looked over the heads of the reception party to the river behind them. There were several steamers tied to the piers, and one caught his eye. Two slender masts rose above the white-painted superstructure and two large paddle wheels, one on each side, sat almost to the stern. On the cover of the wheel facing the shore, in large, ornate, block letters, trimmed in gold, were the words "New York".

Hobart smiled – it had to be an omen, and he was going home.

The small convoy got underway and steamed south, down the James. Before long the river widened and merged into the harbor at Norfolk. Hobart made out the familiar outline of Fortress Monroe, and he readied himself to go ashore. To his surprise, though, the ship did not stop, but passed the fort, headed to the east. The midday sun felt good on their backs, and the westerly breeze pushed them on.

Soon, the ships turned left, heading north, up the Chesapeake Bay, he thought. Puzzled, he approached a sailor, coiling a line on the deck.

"Where are we going?"

The sailor looked up and smirked - "Annapolis, your new home. Camp Parole."

The "New York" tied up in Annapolis, and the men streamed off the ship. It was not a long march to the camp, set up on the grounds of St. John's College, but for many it was still difficult. Before leaving the piers, they bathed, and Hobart watched as some of them threw their clothing and shoes into the mud of St. John's Creek.

Passing the guards at the camp gates, Hobart looked around. At first glance, it did not seem all that different from Belle Isle – crowds of men milling everywhere, many on crutches, some with bandages. A small group of soldiers began to circulate through the crowd, calling out the names of northern states.

"Maine! Maine! Anyone here from Maine?" and "Vermont! New Jersey! Massachusetts!"

Hobart heard a voice calling "New York! New York!" and looking around, shouted "Here! Forty-Fourth New York! Here!"

A man pushed through the crowd and took his hand. "John O'Brien," he said "Sixty-Ninth New York. I'm representing New York here. Let's get out of the mob. " With that, the two pushed to the edge and sat on the ground.

"Where'd you come from?" asked the man, whose accent told Hobart he perhaps was both Irish and from New York City or maybe even Brooklyn. In a few sentences, Hobart told him the story of Yorktown, the Seven Days' and Belle Isle. O'Brien nodded throughout.

"Aye," he said. "There's many here with that same tale. Are you wounded? Sick?"

Hobart shook his head. "Took a shot at Malvern, but I think it's pretty well healed. Could use something to eat, though. " O'Brien laughed. "Sure, and couldn't we all! There will be something before too long. Won't be hardtack and goobers, but we'll grab a root. Here's the what I know. General Dix and the Secesh General Hill are said to be working out the plan, but that might just be camp canard. One of us for one of them, that's the way it's said to be. Sometimes there's a call for fifty or a hundred, and then they leave. Most of the time we just sit around, jawing. The officers will try to hold drill, but some of the peacock soldiers say it's a 'military duty' and they can't do that. Parole says 'no military activity' and they try to make out it's an 'activity' to drill. Stick around us and we'll help you through. Just don't drink the water – you'll get the Tennessee two-step sure as shootin'!"

Hobart tried to take this all in, and over the days that followed he improved. The food, in fact, was a little better and there was more of it.

"I'm trying to remember the last time I had a potato."

"Better not say it too loud, or someone will try to take it from you. Here, have another. "

"Thanks! More beef?"

"Certainly. I don't think I'll ever get my fill of this – not now, not after nothing in the camps."

Many of the men roamed the streets and gardens nearby, helping themselves to vegetables and fruit. One of his new friends returned, his coat bulging. In the privacy of their tent, he opened the jacket and a flood of peaches tumbled onto the cot. Big peaches, ripe and sweet-scented.

Peaches! Wonder what Hoadley is up to?

Hobart avoided most of the crowds – there were gangs forming among the soldiers. He saw a group of them – hard faces, unsmiling, pushing their way through the crowds of soldiers. A man did not move out of their way quickly enough, and he was roughly shoved aside, tumbling to the ground. They bullied the weaker and stole from whoever had anything they thought they wanted. He gave them a wide berth

Finally it was November, and he was called to a tent, where several officers sat behind a table, several boards laid across barrels. They reviewed his record and he was questioned.

"When did you enlist? What regiment?"

"What did you do in the Peninsula campaign?"

"Tell us about Malvern Hill. What about Belle Isle?"

At the end the officers, heads together, conferred. They sat back and the senior of them, a Major, said

"Sergeant, you've served well and faithfully. You're being discharged as disabled due to your injury. You'll be issued passage to take you home. That's all."

He wasn't sure he'd heard the officer correctly.

"I'm sorry, sir, would you say that again?"

The Major relaxed a little.

"Sergeant Walker, you can leave the camp. Your discharge reads that you have a disability due to your wound, and you won't have to serve any longer."

Leaving the room, Hobart stopped by another tent where a young clerk, fingers smudged black with ink, was already completing the form. He pressed a blotter to the last lines and handed it over to him.

"Turn in your equipment to the Quartermaster Sergeant and he will issue you a pass for the railroad back to New York," the clerk intoned without looking up.

He didn't have much equipment to turn in so with what few items he still had tucked away in a knapsack, Hobart collected sixty-eight dollars in pay owed him and left the camp, dressed in a replacement uniform bearing his Sergeant's chevrons and with his "lucky" kepi on his head. As he strode out of Camp Parole, he asked a man leaning against a weathered building

"Which way is the train depot?"

The man scowled at him and jerked a thumb over his shoulder.

"That way".

Hobart nodded and headed off. The man called after him "It's a hike, Yankee – it's all of twenty miles!" and he laughed.

He trudged along the road in the direction the man had indicated. An hour passed, and he wasn't sure he could walk the entire way. He frowned.

"Hey, soldier! Goin' to the depot?"

He looked up. A farm wagon behind two bedraggled mules had stopped. There were four others seated in the back and an old man at the reins.

"I am. Are you headed that way?"

"Sure are. Hop on!"

He clambered up into the bed of the wagon and they bumped and jolted over the rutted roads, past fields that had been harvested and those with the crops still standing, now withered and decaying. There were few people, and those they passed didn't look up as they went by.

The sun was setting they pulled in next to the tracks. Hobart approached the ticket window and, displaying the pass he'd been given, asked about the next train north. The clerk behind the barred opening, head down and busily shuffling papers, said without looking up.

"Tomorrow. Nine in the morning. Maybe" and returned to what evidently was demanding his full attention.

Shaking his head, Hobart turned and walked out. Across the street, a building that seemed intact and proudly bore a battered sign reading "Howard House, Geo. G. Latchford, prop. " For sixty-five cents, he got a reasonably clean room and slept a reasonably sound sleep.

It was cold and blustery in Annapolis that next morning, but Hobart was up, washed, dressed and at the depot by eight. Two others, much like him, stood waiting on the platform, rubbing their hands and stamping against the chill.

"Looks like there's been some fighting here, don't you think?" The man stood next to him. He glanced over. His age, Hobart thought. Thin, very thin. The left sleeve of his coat swung, limp and empty.

"It does, at that." He gestured at a sentry in uniform, musket in his hand, several yards down the platform. "Not taking chances."

The soldier nodded.

"Looky there, behind them trees."

Hobart craned his neck to look. Amid the trunks and bushes he could make out four or five additional soldiers, keeping watch.

At nine the train arrived – a locomotive, coal car, baggage car and coaches. They climbed aboard. At ten the whistle sounded a husky screech and they lurched out of the station.

Baltimore, he thought. *Change for Philadelphia and New York.*

I'll be home by Thanksgiving.

Chapter 8

Brooklyn, New York, November 1862

The wind came out of the northwest, and with it came a cold, sleety rain. Hobart stepped from the train, stretched, and walked along the platform. Without a greatcoat, the uniform sack coat he wore did little to keep out the cold. He shivered as he left the station and, without thinking, followed the long lines of people, heading to the New York ferry. His thoughts drifted back to when he last made this trip, headed in the other direction. He felt a twinge where the bullet wound had healed, but it didn't bother him too much.

He crossed the Hudson without seeing anyone. Businessmen, workers, women, and children jostled and bumped him from every side as the boat chugged across the Hudson. The gulls shrieked, ship's horns bellowed – he heard nothing. He was alone – all alone in his thoughts.

What does a disabled soldier do?

The ferry bumped hard into the slip on the Manhattan shore. Climbing into a carriage, he cross to the piers on the West side and boarded the boat to Brooklyn. His stride quickened and he looked up as he walked along the familiar streets. Passersby glanced curiously at the soldier in the worn uniform, now briskly pacing down De Kalb Avenue. He smiled as he skirted Washington Park's familiar heights. He passed Vanderbilt Avenue, his excitement rising. He turned onto Clinton, the final few blocks ahead of him. It was almost as if time had frozen, he thought. Same streets, same vendors hawking their wares, same familiar smells. Abruptly, he became aware of the bitter scent of coal smoke, the sharp tang of salt air, the pungent smells – now foul, now sweet – that roiled up from the streets. He inhaled deeply and flexed his shoulders, the familiar senses comforting him.

There it is!

Dusk was settling and the street lamps hissed in their golden pools as he reached his boyhood home. Taking the steps two at a time and stopped before the door. He squared his shoulders and knocked. The door swung wide.

"Mother! Mother! It's Hobart! He's home! George! Emma!" Jerome was ecstatic.

A rush of feet and the family descended on him. Elmira, her face more lined than he remembered, held his face in her hands and looked into his eyes, then broke in a broad smile, washed by tears that coursed down her cheeks.

"Welcome home, my son."

They gathered in the parlor and chattered on. Hobart talked of the camps, the food, the marching, the rain, the mud and a little about the fighting. Jerome was particularly interested in what his elder brother had to say and listened intently. They were so engrossed in the conversation that when the front door opened, they jumped. Immediately they all fell silent, and Hobart rose, stepping into the hallway. A man stood with his back to him, placing hat, overcoat and scarf on a coat tree standing there.

"Hello, Father."

Ferdinand spun around and for what seemed to be a long time stared at his son. His eyelids flickered rapidly, and it seemed to be difficult for him to understand what he was seeing.

"Hello, son."

Hobart saw something rare. Tears welled up in his father's eyes and ran down along his cheeks. He stepped forward, held out his arms, and embraced his father – hard.

Elmira and Elizabeth, the immigrant girl who worked with them, scrambled to put together supper – a supper that seemed to interest few of the Walkers that evening. Endless pots of tea before the fire in the parlor, of course, but food? Everyone wanted to talk, and to hear what the soldier had to say. It was late when at last they put out the lights and retreated to bed.

His mother took it as her own personal campaign to create a Thanksgiving feast unrivaled by any they'd ever had.

"What would you have, son? What do you like best?" The newspapers and magazines were replete with the menus of the coming banquet, as presented by the best hotels and restaurants in the city, and she seemed intent on outdoing them all.

"Would you prefer beef? Or turkey? Or ham? Or all of them?"

It couldn't be just "turkey" for him, though – it would have to be "Philadelphia turkey stuffed with chestnuts" or "Braised Oregon Salmon Bardé, Sauce Bernaise". Hobart chuckled. Only once did he hold up a hand.

"Mother, just nothing with 'Virginia' or 'Maryland' in it! Terrapin a la Maryland? No, thank you! I've enjoyed enough of Virginia and Maryland for a bit!"

Giving thanks was never more fervent than in the house on Clinton Street, that November of 1862.

Ferdinand looked up from the letter in his hand.

"Hobart, Stephen said to tell you Mr. Walsh asks if you'll be returning. He still has a position for you."

Hobart thought about it. Buffalo certainly had its appeal. There was a job for him and he had friends. And there was Clara.

He wasn't certain how their relationship, which began so carefully, had evolved over the tumultuous months he'd spent in the Forty-Fourth. He knew that he was eager to get her letters, and felt that she just might be the woman for him. Although her words were warm and personal, she'd never written anything that was specifically romantic. Still, he felt, she was a special person, and the idea of seeing her again, in person, was exciting. He made up his mind. He was going back to Buffalo.

Once again, he made the trek from New York City to Albany, then west to Buffalo, now blanketed deep in winter snow. There was quite a crowd of Walkers on hand to greet him. Stephen, Samuel … everyone in Buffalo, it seemed to him. He carefully folded and packed his uniforms, knotted a cravat around his neck and returned to the life of a civilian.

He looked in the mirror. A man with a level gaze of quiet confidence looked back.

Lost a little weight, have you? Well, Belle Isle would do that to do you.

He smiled slightly, shrugged into his overcoat, and set out for the school where Clara and her mother worked and lived. He knocked, and the door opened. Clara stood in the doorway, the lamplight yellow and warm behind her. She looked and closed her eyes. Suddenly her face exploded into the biggest smile he thought he'd ever seen, her eyes sparkling bright and clear. She held out both her hands.

"Hobart! Er… Mr. Walker! How very nice to see you! Please do come in! Mother! Mr. Walker is here to call on us!"

He stepped into the room just as Clara's mother entered from the kitchen, wiping her hands on a towel at her waist. She, too, held out her hands.

"Mr. Walker! How lovely! We were so worried about you! It is wonderful to have you home!"

She drew him into the parlor, Clara close behind her. The words – not Clara's, but her mother's – echoed in his ears. "We were worried … have you home." She continued –

"Please do sit. You'll have some tea? Delightful! Clara, please see to our guest while I find something for him to eat. He must be famished!" She left the room.

They looked at each other, no one saying a word. Finally, she said in a gentle voice – "Please do sit. We've so much to talk about."

Into the evening they sat in the front parlor. Their conversation, slow at first, picked up quickly, words piling up like a Niagara snowstorm, sentence upon sentence. They talked of his time in Virginia, of Belle Isle, of Camp Parole. They spoke of their friends, conditions in Buffalo, the cost of wheat flour. Without thinking, they drew their chairs closer together, facing each other. He glanced down. They were holding hands.

He couldn't remember a time he had felt such wonder.

The euphoria lasted all of a week. Walking to Mr. Walsh's store, his body bent against the blasting winter wind streaming across the lake, a garish poster in a shop window made him stop.

An upright Union cavalryman, astride a charging horse, sabre drawn, and the single word "Cavalry!" in bold characters at the top. The Twelfth New York Cavalry was being raised, it announced, and good horsemen were wanted. Skipping down the poster, a line at the bottom made him draw a quick, sharp breath.

Under the headline "Bounties" it promised money the state and federal governments would pay to those who joined.

$190. 00 in combined bounties. That's four months' pay – just for joining.

The next column made his eyes open wide. The same enlistment, for a veteran, paid $565. 00.

A years' pay!

He thought of the mud and rain outside Yorktown. With the Confederates retreating quickly toward Williamsburg, the Union infantry couldn't catch them. He remembered the regiment summarily ordered to the ditches along the sloppy roads, and five thousand Federal cavalrymen galloping through, splattering their infantry brothers with Virginia mire.

The evening before, Uncle Stephen had opened a letter from his sister in Michigan. Hobart's cousin Edward Granger had just become an officer in the newly-formed Fifth Michigan Cavalry. If the Michigan branch of the family could, so could the Brooklyn branch.

The cavalry!

It took him only a day to make up his mind. He found the recruiting Sergeant, and presented himself.

"Veteran, you say? Who'd you serve with? Where were you?"

In a few quick sentences, without bravado, he summarized.

Ellsworth's Avengers, the Peninsula Campaign, Malvern Hill, Belle Isle.

At the last, the Sergeant looked at him closely.

"Familiar with horses, are you?"

Drawing a breath, he looked the Sergeant in the eye and said "I learn fast. Quite fast."

The man thought a moment.

"I don't know. Got the experience, that's certain. Cavalry means horses, and you ain't much of a rider. I'll have to ask the Colonel about it."

"Who is the Colonel?"

"Well, Colonel Savage is the Commander, but he's in New York City. Lieutenant Colonel Vought is next, but I won't see him until tomorrow. Let's see – today is Friday. You come back Monday and we'll see what he says."

Hobart nodded, then turned to leave.

"Come back Monday, now!" he repeated, but Hobart was out and in the cold, once again.

After a weekend that felt longer than it was, he returned to the office in West Seneca. This time, though, he didn't come empty-handed. The same Sergeant was there, but another man, with the silver oak leaves of a Lieutenant Colonel on the epaulets of his blue uniform coat stood alongside him. He looked Hobart over carefully, then spoke.

"Sergeant says you'd like to be a cavalryman, but you don't have much experience with horses. Is that so?"

Hobart nodded.

The officer continued "But you do have experience in the field, and being under fire doesn't seem to faze you."

"It does not, sir, it does not."

Scratching his chin, Colonel Vought was silent for a moment, a contemplative look on his face. Hobart decided to play his trump card. He drew a folded paper from his jacket and extended it to the Colonel.

"These gentlemen seem to think I might be of some service."

Vought cocked an eyebrow, took the sheet and unfolded it. He read:

Buffalo, December 13, 1862
Col. P. G. Vought

Sir

The undersigned beg leave to recommend to your favorable notice Hobart Walker, late Sergeant Forty-

Fourth NYVS, with which Reg't he has been connected for the past 18 months. Any position to which he might be assigned we believe him capable of filling with credit to himself and the service.

There followed seventeen ornate signatures and Vought scanned them. He had lived in Buffalo and was familiar with many of them - business, social and religious leaders in the community. Almost against his will, he was impressed. Not many recruits went to this effort to enlist.

He drummed his fingers on the desk top. He looked at Hobart.

"Have to bring you in as a private, you know." Hobart nodded. "Sign here."

Within minutes the clerk-turned-soldier-turned-clerk was a private in Company "D", Twelfth New York Cavalry, the Ira Harris Guard.

* * *

He dashed to Clara's house.

"The cavalry, Hobart? You want to enlist again?" He couldn't mistake the alarm in her voice. She wasn't happy. "Come in, please. I feel we should talk."

They sat in the parlor again, and this time the atmosphere was solemn. He tried to explain.

"It's my duty, Clara! Men are being called all the time! I know how to do this, and I feel as though I should be with them."

Finally, she stood.

"I think perhaps you might go now. Allow me to think about this, and we'll speak again. Can you call tomorrow, in the afternoon?" He nodded.

"Very well, then. Until tomorrow." There was no warmth in her voice.

* * *

It was gray and gloomy as he approached her door, matching his mood. She opened it and motioned him in.

Again, they sat in the parlor, both sitting erect and stiff. Her face was set. After a moment of terrible silence, she spoke.

"Hobart, I did not sleep well last night. I thought and thought about this past year, and what you say you'll do now. To be candid, sir, I was terrified the entire time you were away. Your letters were so cheerful and happy, but they did not match what we read in the newspapers. When you went south to the Peninsula, I prayed every day – every single day – that God would watch over you and keep you safe. When we heard that you had been taken prisoner, I wept. I wept again when you were released, and was thrilled when your letter said you were returning to Buffalo. I dreamed wonderful dreams about what we might be – together. And now, you tell me you wish to go back."

She paused. He knew, without knowing how, what would follow. He felt a roaring in his ears, and his hands shook, ever so little.

"Hobart, I cannot allow a man to court me if he is not near me. After everything that has happened, I fear I could not stand another year, another month, another day like that. Should you decide to remain here, in Buffalo, my heart would overflow. If you feel that you must go ..." She paused, closed her eyes, then opened them, looking directly into his. "... then you must go. But I cannot, in any way, go with you. I simply cannot. You must choose."

Again, that dreadful, terrible, roaring silence in the room. His head dropped, and he inhaled a deep, deep breath. He stood.

"I understand, Miss Williams, truly I do. Please give my warm regards to your mother."

He did not look back, or see her eyes as he left, closing the front door behind him.

*   *   *

Arriving in Fort Washington on the northern shore of Staten Island, Hobart began his cavalry training. Even as the winter winds whistled across lower New York Harbor to rake Staten Island unabated, the troops were out on the parade fields.

He, and the others, began with the "school of the trooper – dismounted", the as-yet unmounted soldiers sought to master the basic infantry movements.

I know this. I can do this in my sleep.

He remembered his early days in the Seventy-Fourth, and Sergeant Adams helping him along the way. In the evening, while the gales blew in from the Atlantic, he gathered the recruits around him.

"Let's do this again. Here's the rifle movement."

They were issued equipment and arms – new arms. He hefted the Burnside carbine.

Lighter than the Springfield. No bayonet, either.

A curved cavalryman's sabre and a new revolver

Not a Walker, though.

Throughout the bitter winter he worked on the basic maneuvers. In the off-time, he avoided the card games and horseplay of the younger soldiers and spent time at the stables.

* * *

The scar on his left side stung a little as he hefted a full fork of horse manure out of the stall, onto the cart awaiting. Another.

"Can't get over it, Private. Why would you want to come down here, on your own, to shovel horse dung?"

"I told you. You teach me about horses, I help a little where I can."

The wizened stable hand shook his head, but he was smiling.

"Ain't seen nothing like it. Soldier shoveling horse manure when he don't have to. Beats all."

* * *

"Hey, Hobart!" The voice rang through the barracks. Private Walker turned his head.

"Sam Tanner!"

The old friends met in a hug.

"Look at you! All dressed up, gold braid, Lieutenant bars! What are you doing here, anyway?"

"You're looking at First Lieutenant Samuel W. Tanner, Twelfth New York Cavalry, the Ira Harris Guards!"

"What company are you going to be in?"

"They haven't assigned me yet, but I should ask for yours. You need someone to keep you line and keep you from getting shot … again!"

The idea of serving with his friend put a smile on Hobart's face. He redoubled his efforts to learn and what it would take to be a soldier on horseback.

*   *   *

Late in March Hobart was called into Colonel Savage's quarters. The Colonel was standing with his back to the door when Private Walker entered but turned to face him.

"Stand easily, Private" and Hobart relaxed slightly.

A bright blaze crackled in the fireplace behind him, silhouetting Savage against its light.

"Private Walker, you've done well with the Twelfth. Lieutenant Colonel Vought told me of your eagerness to join us, and it seems his approval was well-founded."

Hobart was not sure where this compliment was headed, but he bowed his head slightly, acknowledging the praise. Savage continued –

"The Regiment is expanding, and we will need skilled leaders with experience under fire. I'm moving you from Company "D" to Company "I". Furthermore, I'm promoting you to Lieutenant. Congratulations, Lieutenant Walker. I think you'll want to get a new uniform coat" and he smiled a small smile.

Hobart took a moment to digest what he'd just heard, then couldn't hide his pleasure.

"Thank you kindly, sir. I'll not let you down."

Savage, already turning back to the fire, nodded absently.

"I'm sure you won't, Walker. You might want to get another cap."

Another cap?

Then he grinned. He knew that cavalry officers wore the kepi of the enlisted man, but they also wore broad-brimmed slouch hats with gold-and-yellow braid. He'd get one, certainly, but he wasn't about to give up the kepi he'd worn for so long.

Returning to the company, his messmates congratulated him with the rough humor of soldiers

"Glad to be rid of you!"

"You'd never make a dragoon, anyway – too much of a ground-pounder in you!"

Under it all, though, they were pleased for him.

"Let me gather my traps, and I'll be out of your hair!"

As he moved to the Company "I" area he took a detour through the area assigned to "E" Company, where Tanner was assigned. He found his old friend, presented an exaggerated salute and casually asked -

"Excuse me, Lieutenant, can you share with me where a reputable haberdasher might be found? One who might properly attire an officer in the cavalry of our great nation? A new Second Lieutenant, perhaps?"

Tanner looked at him quizzically, then caught on. He grabbed his friend and fellow veteran in an excited hug. He, too, was glad to see this promotion.

Spring began to push winter out of Staten Island and the pace of training quickened. Manuals of arms, target practice, sabre drills with arms sore and aching became the order of the day. When mounted, they drilled with the horses. Trot to trot-out, trot to gallop, maneuvering as a platoon, as a troop and as a squadron, leaping fences and ravines – from daylight until the sun's setting they drilled, and a growing sense of expectancy grew throughout the camp.

When he could, Hobart boarded the ferry that ran from the north side of the island to Manhattan Island, transferred to cross the East River and spend a furlough at home. Ferdinand and Elmira were always delighted to see him, and his siblings thrilled in the stories the young officer had to tell them. At night, after they all had gone to bed, the three boys – Hobart, Jerome and George – stayed awake. The younger boys could not get enough of his tales, and badgered him to tell and retell of the exciting times in the field.

"Tell about Yorktown, Hobart! Tell us about the time your hat saved your life!"

"It didn't exactly save my life, but it was close. Listen, and I'll tell you!" and they never tired of listening.

*   *   *

The day was warm and sunny. A gentle breeze blew in from the ocean, and puffs of white cloud gamboled across the sky. They had been on the range that morning, and the men had fired unusually well. Things were definitely looking good. Just after dinner, runners from Colonel Savage's office ran through the camp. Calling out the names of various officers.

"Boyce! Cooper! Meech! Spink! Stearns! Walker! Weller!"

"What's up?

"The Colonel wants you in his office – now."

Entering the building that served as the Colonel's quarters and Regimental headquarters, he saw the others, and they all looked at each other curiously, unsure of why they were here. Awaiting the commander, Hobart considered the group. He knew them all, some better than others. There was Moses Boyce, a 41-year old junior officer from Company "C". Alanson Welles from Company "F" and Robert Meech from "E" Company – Sam Tanner's company. Colonel Savage entered and the men snapped to attention.

Without preliminary, he put them at ease.

"Gentlemen, I take no pleasure in what I am here to say to you. The Brigade has consolidated several regiments and we find ourselves with more Second Lieutenants than we are authorized. I have requested that we be allowed that surplus, but my request has been denied. We drew names by lottery, and you were the ones drawn. The Army cannot keep you in this unit as enlisted cavalrymen – that would be awkward for everyone.

I am authorized to allow you to transfer to other units, but as infantry privates, not as officers. If you choose, you may accept discharge by reason of consolidation, and there would be no objection to your enlisting again at a later date. I am sorry, gentlemen. The adjutant will accept your decisions and issue your documents. Thank you for your dedication to the Ira Harris Guard. " He turned and left.

The seven stunned officers looked at each. No one spoke. All the training, the practice, the riding and jumping had come to naught. Not only were they out of the cavalry, they were out of the army. Slowly, one by one, they shuffled from the room.

Chapter 9

Brooklyn, New York. July 1863

Combative gray and white gulls quarreled, swooping and diving as the ferry steamed across New York Harbor, past Governor's Island, and tied up at the southern tip of Manhattan. The harbor was its usual orchestra of ship's whistles, clank and clatter of machinery, and hundreds of shouting voices. Hobart didn't see any of it, didn't hear anything. His gaze was locked on the deck of the boat, and his mind a blank. In a fog, he walked to the ferry slip to Brooklyn, rode the short trip across to the east side, and walked home. In the late June sun, children played in the streets, laughing and calling. Men in bowler hats and tweed caps, women clutching parasols to shield their pale faces walked briskly along. No one noticed the discharged cavalryman trudging down the familiar streets, oblivious to his surroundings.

There was no excited reception when he arrived home, and the evenings were quiet. He knew the family was avoiding talk about the army, but gradually the tension eased.

Hobart looked up as the front door opened and Jerome came down the hallway and into the kitchen.

"How was school? Learning how to save the world?"

Jerome smiled. "I'll have to master chemistry and physiology before I can do any world saving. There is a lot to this." He joined his elder brother at the kitchen table and they chatted, tea cups rattling. "How was your day?"

"Took a walk. Climbed up to Fort Washington …"

"Again? You should pitch a tent up there, as much as you go."

Hobart grunted. "Went there today, and for the first time, I think, saw Staten Island. It struck me that the boys in the Twelfth were about ready to move into the field, and they'd be riding without me."

"It's hard, isn't it?"

"It is, Jerome. I was ready … I was really ready to go. And then – nothing."

He rattled the pages of the "Daily Eagle". There was fighting, he read, a major battle in Pennsylvania, and he devoured every word. One article said the 44th New York had been in the very center of it, and the casualty list was long.

He read it anxiously, wincing at the names he knew.

The post office had a letter for him. A letter from Sam.

We're packing things up here, and expect to be on the ship right soon. North Carolina, they say.

He crumpled the page, his frustration mounting.

*   *   *

Brooklyn, New York July 4, 1863

Hobart awoke to cheering crowds in the streets outside. He dressed quickly and ran downstairs to the kitchen. His brothers sat at the table, coffee cups in hand.

"Lots of excitement out there today. More so than normal, d'you think?"

"Could well be, Hobart. Independence Day and defeating 'Marse Robert' at Gettysburg? Oh, I'd say they'd be celebrating. Are we going to the park?"

As they had for so many years, the trio perched atop the hill at Washington Park when the sun set that evening, thrilling to the wild display of exuberant fireworks bursting over Battery Park.

* * *

Within just a few days, though, there were more fireworks in New York, but they weren't celebratory. From the heights of Brooklyn, the Walker brothers watched in horrified disbelief.

"What are they doing, Hobart?" George looked from the flames in Manhattan to his brother.

"I don't know, George, I really can't understand it … not at all! Why people would not only refuse to answer their country's call, but then turn that call into an excuse for such despicable activities? There are men – many men! – out in the field as volunteers, and these people won't go? I heard that the Governor had called in the Seventy-Fourth, my very first unit, to restore order. I'm beginning to think that New York is not where I want to be."

He and Ferdinand walked in the summer twilight.

"Father, what am I to do? This is not where I thought I'd find myself, and I simply am at a loss. What shall I do?"

Ferdinand pondered the question for several moments before he answered carefully

"Son, that is something perhaps only you can answer. You have certainly done your duty, and more cannot be asked of you. Had you considered perhaps returning to Buffalo?"

"I had, but I do not think it would be fair, at this point, to impose again on Uncle Stephen. There must be some place I can go where I might contribute something, only I don't know where that might be." He said nothing about Clara, and Ferdinand did not ask.

* * *

In the late summer, Ferdinand left New York on a business trip for the A. T. Stewart company. He had begun to visit retail stores in other cities as the company expanded from one retail location in Manhattan into a larger wholesale enterprise. On his return, he seemed uncharacteristically chipper. He took Hobart by the arm and the two strolled through the Brooklyn neighborhood.

"You would so love the places I've seen – the places I've been. Towns and villages springing up throughout the land. Businesses booming, railroads going everywhere! And the thing I hear – time after time - no one seems to be able to find good employees. The war has taken the young men. Son, you've served, and with honor, too. You need not do more, and you can begin building a good life for yourself. You may well find a fine young woman and start a family."

Ferdinand continued "I can tell you of many good businesses, run by reputable, honest gentlemen, where you could begin immediately. You are adventuresome and love the outdoors, and the way the prairie stretches out in front of you – well, I feel you would be quite satisfied. "

Hobart thought carefully before he answered his father.

"It may well be that my future does lie elsewhere. With Ada in Ohio, it wouldn't be as if I would be without any family, either."

For the first time in many weeks, there was a sparkle in his eyes. His stride was strong and purposeful, and his smile ready. For a week or more, he grilled Ferdinand daily, asking many questions about businesses, locations, jobs. The more they spoke, the more he seemed drawn to a pair of opportunities – a newly established general goods store in Minnesota and a grain mill in Adel, Iowa.

"Rochester is small but it is established and growing. The Iowa town is smaller, but I feel it has great, untapped potential. This grain mill sits on the North Racoon River, and with all the farm land for many miles around, should grow. There is a railroad, but construction has been impeded by this war. When it is over, I feel the town will expand rapidly. Either one would be a good choice, but Rochester seems to be something that would suit you sooner."

Hobart thought about it. He took a breath and made his choice. Rochester. He packed away his uniforms, his "lucky" kepi, and became part of the population of the growing Minnesota town. One day there might be a Walker in Adel, but now it would be Minnesota.

*   *   *

Throughout the autumn and into the winter of 1863 – 64 he worked diligently at Frederick's store. He joined a church, made friends quickly and seemed happy in his new position.

Rochester, MN Dec 6/1863

My Dear Mother

I received your kind letter some time ago and it is so seldom that I receive a letter from you personally that I ought to have showed my appreciation of it by writing to you ere this but when one is occupied in the store from 7 AM until 8 ½ or 9 PM they don't feel much like writing. I received Geo's letter written last Sunday this morning & will answer it soon. So you did not have a Thanksgiving gathering in Brooklyn. I had turkey, etc., out here but with all my imagination could not make it feel like home. I find that there is a vast difference between eating such a meal at a boarding house & at home. T. W. Sr. has moved into his new house and I board with him. T. W's girl is indeed a fine looking little girl. She is sadly afflicted. Her right side is paralyzed and her mind is left just as it was, when she was taken sick some 6 years ago. I have sometimes thought that a cure was possible. She understands any common sentences and knows when she does right or wrong, and has a peculiar way of showing joy & pleasure. She is, of course, unable to speak or articulate freely but I have no doubt that she could at least be very much improved.

We expect & hope to be in our new church next Sunday but will be there all events by Christmas. It is a neat little church capable of holding from 180 to 200 persons. I called this afternoon on a Mrs. Musson from Butternuts, she was married about 2 years ago & knew Ada very well before her marriage. She told me her maiden name but I have forgotten it. Mr. Gambria had a letter today from his son William who is now in Mexico. He was so badly used as to feel glad to & lucky to get out of Texas as he did. He has been imprisoned and ironed two or three times and is very bitter against the secessionists. He describes the state of things as awful in the extreme.

Tell Jerome that I will answer his French letter as soon as I can find time, that it takes more time to compose such a letter & that just now my time is limited. Cornelia wants me to tell you that she has me under her eye & thinks by good management to make something of me yet. Remember me to all friends included the "Dillars!

When Father sends my overcoat, if you have a shirt or anything of that kind that I have left please forward it. Tell Father to please keep an eye on my bounty papers as I expect they will be worth something soon! Write soon.

Your aff Son,
Hobart M. Walker

∗   ∗   ∗

He pulled the collar of his coat together beneath his chin and wrapped a woolen scarf around his neck. December temperatures had plummeted into the twenties, and it seemed to him as if he could never stop shivering. His new church was open, and he was eager to make the short walk from his boarding house there. At least the stone walls would break the constant, biting wind.

At the red doors, he paused as another young man walked up the stone path behind him.

Hobart saw that he was dressed neatly, but there was no escaping the obvious – he walked on crutches and the left leg of his trousers was pinned up high on his thigh. The lad seemed about his age, but his face was drawn and his eyes seemed flat and lifeless. He looked at Hobart and Hobart returned his gaze.

Without a word, he knew. Another veteran. After the service, he sought out the young man and they chatted briefly. After a few moments of conversation, Hobart nodded toward the man's missing leg.

"Army?" he asked.

The man glanced down, laughed without mirth and replied "Yep, First Minnesota. You?"

Hobart pulled his coat tighter against the raw wind.

"Forty-Fourth New York and, for a while, Twelfth New York Cavalry."

There was a moment's silence, and in that quiet a bond united the two. Whatever they were, wherever they had come from, they were linked as veterans, and in an instant were brothers. The lad went on

"Mustered in April of '61. From then on, it seemed as if we'd never get out of the field. Bull Run, Balls Bluff, Berryville, Yorktown, West Point, Hanover Court House, Fair Oaks, Peach Orchard, Savage Station, White Oak Swamp, Glendale, Malvern Hill …" his voice trailed off.

Softly, Hobart said "I was at Yorktown … Malvern Hill, too. Caught a Minié ball there and found myself the guest of the graybacks at Belle Isle."

The man looked up sharply and his eyes searched Hobart's face. "Paroled?"

Hobart nodded. "Might just as well have stayed at the island," he laughed dryly.

The man went on, a little bit more spirit in his tone. "We got through all of that and I was beginning to think I'd make it until Gettysburg." Again he paused. Hobart didn't prod him, but the other man continued, almost to himself. "Hot as Hell. Just as hot as the very doors of Hell itself, that day. We were in the center when Longstreet charged. The line buckled and came near to breaking, but we held 'em off. They fell back and we thought maybe that was it. That last day, though, Pickett came across the field with a division of madmen. They just kept coming and coming … I'd never seen anything like it. Don't know how many rounds I'd fired when it just went black. Woke up in an ambulance wagon and that's when they said my leg was gone. Artillery. Solid shot, I think."

Again he paused, then looked up. "Could have been worse, though, hey?" and managed a tight smile. "They're gonna give me a wooden leg, they say. If I can follow a plow and get rid of these things," and he gestured with the crutches, "I'll be all right."

Hobart held out his hand. "You will. You truly will" he said. They shook hands, two strong young men in the cold December light.

"You take care," said the lad.

"You, too. Merry Christmas." The man nodded.

"Merry Christmas to you." His crutches made a staccato tapping on the stones as he walked away.

*　　*　　*

The lamps were already lighted on a bitterly cold January afternoon when the door to Frederick's opened and a gentleman approached Hobart at the counter. At first he thought it was a boy, until the man looked up at him and began to speak. Hobart quickly realized this gentleman was in full manhood, and his clipped British accent said he was not native to the Midwestern plains. His piercing blue eyes looked up at Hobart as he said

"My good fellow. I shall be opening a medical office here and will need various supplies. I'm told that you would be able to help me procure them."

Hobart nodded politely. "Certainly, sir. What is it you'll need? Bandages, splints?"

The man shook his head. "Oh, dear, no. I shan't be doing much surgery, I should think. I'll be conducting physical examinations for the Army – young men joining for this war. Just basic office supplies." He handed Hobart a list, each item written in impeccable copperplate script. "Have that sent 'round when it's ready, would you?"

"I'll be honored to ensure you get these things promptly," he answered. "To whom shall I send the invoice?"

The man drew himself up to his full height, which was well below that of Hobart. "Dr. Mayo," he answered proudly. "Dr. William Mayo." Turning on his heel, he left the store.

*　　*　　*

The Christmas celebration had ended, and winter settled on Rochester. Biting, gray, choking winter. Each day, Hobart trudged back and forth between the boarding house and Frederick's, and every day the trek seemed to grow longer. By mid-January, he was sure he could not remain. He walked briskly into the small room he occupied, packed his belongings, and left Minnesota.

*   *   *

Cleveland, Ohio Feb 24/64

My Dear Mother

As you can see I am still in Cleveland, where I have been very busy the last week helping Ada in her preparations for the sanitary fair, which is now in progress. It is certainly as far as the looks of it are concerned, a magnificent success. What the proceeds will be, is yet to be seen. Ada flourishes as a Spaniard, and a very good Spanish Lady she makes, too.

As for myself I am still a visitor at Ada's house, but will join the army in about a week, probably.

No doubt, my dear Mother, the step may seem an unwise one for me to take when I was so well situated as I was at Frederick's but I could not stay in that country without injury to my health. And you have long known my antipathy to a store, I must have out-door employment.

And at no time has my country needed me so much as at present. She needs every man that can be spared, and I am going at her call. I hesitated some time after I had made up mind, but I thought that Aunt P. Ann had given two sons and that now the third one had left her. And although I knew that you would no doubt feel as if I were foolish to go back where I had been served so the first time, still I thought that I was the only one in the family liable to military duty, and it would be no more than doing my share, even if I never returned, which of course I expect to.

I have certainly seen all the different phases of a soldier's life, so that no one can say that I do not know what is before me. And besides it is against the law to discourage enlistment.

Has Father arrived home yet, and what success did he have? I was in hope he would return this way.

Write soon Mother & direct care of Jarvis and remember where I am

I am your aff't son,
Hobart

They sat on the porch, as winter left Cleveland at last, and warmer breezes drifted in off the Lakes. Jarvis Adams, Ada's husband, passed Hobart a glass.

"Try this – it's a new beverage."

Hobart took a sip.

"My! That has some spirit! What is it?"

Jarvis chuckled. "Called 'ginger beer', but there's no alcohol in there, or not much, anyway. So, where were we?"

"Jarvis, I almost want to stop reading the 'Morning Leader.' I'm tasked with reading the intelligence about arriving shipments and the like, but I keep seeing stories about the war. I read a story not long ago about an Ohio man, a Captain, who actually tunneled out of Libby Prison. That caught my eye, you can imagine!"

Jarvis nodded. "Take you back, did it?"

"Indeed! I appreciate your efforts to find me a position, and a good position it is, too. It's just that I cannot seem to get away from the war. It makes me very uncomfortable to be sitting at ease here, when men are still being drafted for the army. "

"What are you thinking?"

"I'm not certain. I keep feeling I should be in uniform, but I don't know if I should enlist here, or go back to New York, or what I might do."

Jarvis thought for a moment.

"You know, they are raising another regiment in the city. The old 29th National Guard Regiment has been renamed the 150th Ohio Volunteer Infantry, and the word is they'll be going to Washington. The enlistment is only one hundred days, and one of my law partners is a Lieutenant. I'm sure he could get you a space there. Maybe a hundred days would answer your question. We could certainly hold your position for you."

"That's Jason, isn't it? Jason Canfield? Married to Cousin Mary?"

Jarvis nodded.

Hobart sipped at the ginger beer.

A hundred days. That's less than what I spent in Albany. Maybe that would answer my question.

He set the glass down and looked at his brother-in-law.

"I believe I'll take it, Jarvis. Thank you."

In less than a month, Hobart, Company "D" and the rest of the Regiment was on the move, headed for the nation's capital. To the tune of a brass band lustily playing patriotic airs, the Regiment marched to the railroad depot. Passing the ruins of the Union Depot, destroyed earlier that year in a major fire, the soldiers were herded up a temporary platform and onto the waiting railroad cars, on the way to Washington and, they hoped, glory. Hobart, with the jaundiced eye of the veteran, had his own view of the matter. Shortly after arriving at Fort Saratoga, an artillery battery northeast of the capital, Hobart wrote to Jerome.

> Fort Saratoga
> Sunday, June 5th, 1864
>
> My Dear Brother
>
> Your letter was received a day or two ago, and indeed I was very glad to hear from you. By the bye there is one young man here whom you know. His name is Gib Brayton, he is a nephew of the Rev J. R's and a citizen of Cleveland. He says he wants you to write to him, his address is the same as mine. We have received orders to get 5 days rations

ready, and Madame Rumor says we leave here in a day or two, for the Front. I have learnt during my career as a soldier that Madam R does not always tell the truth, but rather think she is reliable this time. "on dit" that we go to the White House, which you know is on the Pamunkey River. I for one am not sorry, I want to see this militia do some service. I came out expecting it, and shall not be disappointed. Going to the White House may not be going under fire, still it is fairly near it, and I should not wonder if we would see a little of it.

I received that letter that came through Father's hands yesterday. It was from Sam Tanner. He is asst Paymaster in the Navy and he is coming home in July. I mean to go back with him as Clerk. It is at a salary of about $700 to $800 and prize money, and I should not wonder if I would take it. I have been with him both in Cavalry and Infantry and would like to try a trip in the Navy with him. Here I am learning Heavy Artillery and all together I have quite an extended experience in Uncle Sam's service. There goes the drum – Adieu.

Direct as before,
Hobart
Co. D Direct 150th OVI
Washington DC

His complacency was short-lived. Captain Wizeman called the company together. The men squatted on the ground or leaned against the massive cannons as he spoke.

"Men, we're hearing that General Jubal Early, with a force of several thousand, is moving north through the Shenandoah Valley. Lee's ordered him to drive Union troops from the Valley, take the food there, destroy the railroad line to Washington and threaten the capital. We're here to see that he doesn't do that! The Corps wants us packed and moved over to Fort Stevens. Wants us there by morning. Get moving!"

Chattering with excitement, the men clustered in groups.

"We're ready for 'em!"

"Bring on the rebs!"

"We'll drive 'em out and all the way to Richmond!"

Hobart watched, saying nothing. His glance was bemused, thinking he'd heard this before. In fact, he could hear his own voice, in the distance from the early days in Albany, saying these very things. He pulled his kepi low over his eyes and turned away.

"Where you going, Hobart?" A middle-aged private, his blue uniform coat still new, held his arm out to stop him.

Hobart looked at him, almost with pity.

"I'm going to make sure my rifle is clean, my bayonet is sharp, and that I've got a pouch full of cartridge and caps. If the secesh do come this way, you're going to need more than bluster and big words to stop them."

The man dropped his arm and stepped away.

It was mid-afternoon and hot, a brilliant sun beating directly down on the defenses. A Union picket, deployed beyond the fort's perimeter, first raised the alarm with the cry "Rebs comin'!". Quickly, the other pickets and the skirmish line dashed back to the safety of the earthen embankments.

Captain Wizeman ordered the company to man the cannon but was summarily rebuffed by the artillery officer.

"Look," he exclaimed to Wizeman, "we're the artillery, we know what's to do. You men keep the Rebs beyond rifle range and we'll take care of them!"

The Ohio captain pulled his men back and repositioned along the man-made ridges.

"Pick your shots, boys, and make 'em keep their heads down!" The gray line, their artillery pieces behind them, moved closer.

True to their word, the cannoneers, men from Massachusetts and Pennsylvania, sighted their big guns and opened fire. The infantrymen of company D watched in horrified fascination as shells, solid shot and canister rained down on the gray lines. They saw men fall by the dozens, and their mouths fell open in shock.

Southern sharpshooters took up positions in homes and business buildings nearby, and the unprotected artillery men began to fall.

"That house! The one right they-ah! See it?" An artillery captain roared. There was no mistaking the New England in his enraged voice.

"They got sharpshooters in there! Get a gun on it! Knock it down!"

A gun crew swiveled their Parrott rifled cannon and trained the black iron barrel on the offending structure.

"Fire! Fire at will!"

The gun roared and bucked viciously backward. The gun crew stabilized it and, with practiced strokes, reloaded.

"You! Bring another gun on it!" A second cannon turned.

Pointing with his sabre, the officer thundered.

"Get rounds on those houses! Now!"

The cannoneers scrambled through their deadly ballet and the gunners yanked the fuse cords. Both field guns fired, then fired again. Spinning the elevation screw, the crews fired, their shells tracing a line directly into the buildings. The first shell struck it without detonating, but all the successive rounds burst on impact. The house collapsed, timbers and debris flying wildly.

"Good! Now, take that other house – the one over there!"

On each gun, six men lifted the heavy stock and heaved the weapons around. The gunners slid their sights into the mounts and squinted through, motioning the guns slightly left or right. Moments later, both fired again. And again. A third salvo and the second building collapsed, flames licking out of the wreckage. Hobart heard voices screaming.

Down the line, he saw a regiment of soldiers – one of the New York regiments, he thought – fixing their bayonets and preparing to move against the Confederates. He breathed a silent prayer for them.

Then, behind him, men began to cheer. A few, at first, then hundreds.

"Hurrah!" They shouted.

"Hurrah for President Lincoln!"

To his amazement, Hobart saw a carriage and four horses stop behind the parapets. A woman and several men sat in it and, when it had stopped one of the men stood and clambered down. A tall man – a very tall man, wearing tall top hat. Unmistakable. Abraham Lincoln, the President of the United States, had come to Fort Stevens.

The men gaped in amazement, and the officers hurried to get their attention.

"Men! There's graybacks out there! To your guns!"

Reluctantly, they turned back to the fight, but more than once, a soldier sneaked a glance at the President, standing atop the fortifications, next to one of the Massachusetts artillery batteries. He seemed completely unruffled by the noise and carnage in front of him.

Then, a sharp "ping!" as something ricocheted off a cannon. An officer standing nearby clutched his leg and, with a cry, fell to the ground. Others, standing nearby, ran to where he lay.

"A surgeon! Get a surgeon!"

A young Lieutenant looked down at the fallen soldier.

"That is the surgeon!" Lincoln looked on, his face softened in sympathy for the writhing man on the ground. A group lifted him and carried him back to safety behind the earthen wall.

A voice – no one knew who it was – shouted angrily.

"Get down from there, you damn fool!"

At this, another man, a short, stocky man wearing fashionable sideburns and a very long, pointed beard, ran up to the President.

Hobart turned to the man beside him.

"Who is that fellow? Looks familiar, doesn't he?"

The man grunted, slamming his ramrod down the barrel of his Springfield.

"Dunno. Stanton, mebbe?"

Whoever it was, he strode up to the President and, face flushed and red, shouted at him.

"Mr. President, you must leave! Now! If you do not, I shall be compelled to call an ambulance and force you to go!"

Lincoln looked at him for a moment and, without a word, stepped down off the berm, behind the lines of soldiers still firing at the Confederates. As he walked past Hobart, he paused for a moment.

"I thought I was the Commander in Chief." His voice sounded wistful, almost boyish. Hobart grinned at him.

"You are, sir. You are!"

Lincoln's mouth twitched and he patted Hobart's shoulder.

"Thank you, son. Stay strong." And he was gone.

Hobart turned away and squinted down the long barrel of his rifle. It was the first time he had faced fire since Malvern Hill, but he never paused. With practiced ease, he flipped up the rear sight and aligned it on a Confederate soldier, a hundred yards or so distant. Without thinking, the hours and hours of training took over. He breathed deeply, squeezed the trigger and the musket roared, kicking back hard into his shoulder. The dense and swirling cloud of blue smoke cleared, and he saw the Confederate fall. Without pause, he dropped the rifle butt to the ground, reloaded, and looked for another target.

The Confederate lines moved closer to the fort, then paused. There was another volley from behind the fort's walls and Hobart glanced around. Lines – long lines – of Union soldiers filed into the area behind them.

"Halt!" The blue lines stopped.

"Left, FACE!" As one, the men pivoted, now behind the Ohio men.

"Take positions!" They moved up to the embankments.

Hobart turned to the man on his right and smiled.

"These boys know what they're doing. Watch 'em and learn!"

"Fire at will!" The familiar crackle of musket fire rippled all along the line. Gray-clad soldiers fell.

From behind him, Hobart heard voices calling "Fix bayonets!" Breathing deeply, he pulled the long blade from its leather scabbard, twisted it onto the muzzle of his rifle, and grasped the stock. On both sides, the inexperienced men fumbled with their bayonets, unsure of the procedure. Grunting, Hobart leaned his rifle against a mound and moved quickly among them, helping first one and then another, exhorting them the whole time. A grizzled Corporal from one of the veteran units looked at him, nodded and smiled. Hobart smiled back, a tight, brief smile – he was with his own.

"Charge!"

The union artillery, pouring grapeshot and shrapnel into the Confederate ranks, wreaked bloody havoc among them. The guns thundered in Hobart's ears as they hurled their horrible rain. Early's men were fierce and determined fighters and turned to face the rushing lines of blue. In the horrible melee that followed, Virginian grappled with New Yorker, Georgian with Ohioan. Blood pooled on the ground until, at last, the men in gray broke off and retreated. The battle of Fort Stevens was over, and Jubal Early had been denied.

"Hurrah! Hurrah!" Their cheers echoed all along the line. The Hundred and Fiftieth Ohio, and others just like them, had faced veteran, skilled soldiers, and turned them back. They returned to their camps, exhausted but elated. Hobart picked up two letters from the adjutant. He sat down on an empty keg and tore open the first envelope. Another Ohio soldier, his face streaked with sweat and black powder, stopped and looked over his shoulder.

"From home? All good, I trust."

Hobart read a few lines and turned to him, his face lined and drawn. He shook his head slowly.

"From my sister, in Cleveland. Seems another cousin is gone. Edward, a Michigan boy – cavalry. Died at Front Royal. Just over there." He gestured weakly toward the west. "That's another. My Aunt Phoebe's lost three sons. Disease, but they're just as dead as if a secesh bullet found them. Another one – my cousin Eugene – fell at Yazoo City last March. I know this is everyone's war, but the Walkers seem to be paying a steep price."

The trooper put a hand on his shoulder. It rested there for just a moment, and then he walked away. Hobart finished reading Ada's letter, folded it carefully, and put it in his coat.

*　　*　　*

With the threat posed by Jubal Early gone, the Ohio regiment returned to Fort Slocum. Two weeks later, their 100-day enlistment expired, the soldiers of the 150th returned to Cleveland. One evening they were standing post on the defenses walls, and the following morning on trains, bound up the Susquehanna Valley away from Virginia and home to Ohio. Stepping down from the cars in Cleveland, the militia marched with flags waving and music playing, ignoring a steady downpour, to Public Square. There, in a festive setting with Lake Erie to the north and the Cuyahoga River to the west, the Soldiers Aid Society of Cleveland hosted them to dinner and a welcoming ceremony. The festivities concluded, they returned again to Camp Cleveland where, the regiment was disbanded and the men discharged. They were civilians again.

Chapter 10

Cleveland, Ohio August 1864

With a great sigh of escaping steam, the train groaned to a stop at the Cleveland station. Hobart watched as the door of the first freight car was slid back and workmen, already sweating in the morning sun, began to unload. The first car was filled with barrels stenciled "Minnesota". He pried up a board and looked. Dried white beans. The next, heavy bundles of woolen cloth, and the next crude iron ingots. Hobart counted each item carefully and checked it against the list he was holding. It would be a long day.

When he returned from Fort Stevens, he was determined to build a civilian career, and he began diligently. His efforts did not go unnoticed.

"Hey, Walker!" Jim Petrie, supervising the unloading, called to him. "It's a hot one today! Don't feel you have to do it all by noon!"

Hobart nodded, and returned to the freight cars.

Mid-morning, they took a break. A boy brought a bucket of cold water along the platform, and everyone dipped a cup. In the shade, they chatted.

"You're catching on fast," one of his colleagues said. "Took me weeks to figure out this system."

"Yeah," chimed another. "We'll all be working for Hobart in a month!"

The kidding was good-natured, but it was clear they respected him.

This could be worse, I suppose. Wish I could be excited about it. It's not like being in the field.

He did have his ritual. Each day, on his way to work, he bought a copy of the "Cleveland Morning Leader" from a little boy on the street corner. While others in the office chatted over their lunches or during surreptitious breaks, he scanned the headlines and read. He skipped past market reports, society columns and advertisements for men's wear, always looking for the column "Latest News by Telegraph". There he found what really interested him – news from the fronts.

They sat in the shade of the station, dinner pails open.

"What's the headline today, Hobart?"

"Well, Grant is still pushing Lee hard. Says here that Sherman is marching on Atlanta. "

"Think it will be over soon?"

"I don't know – the Secesh fight pretty fierce. I really liked General McClellan, but I must say that Grant seems much more of a fighter. They're pushing in the Shenandoah, too. I guess they don't want Rebs coming back at Washington."

As the humid Ohio summer waned, it became increasingly difficult for Hobart to keep focused on his accounts and his ledgers.

"I don't know, Ada, it just seems so hard to keep my mind on working."

They sat on the porch, out of the sun. There was a large glass pitcher of lemonade on the table, and ice tinkled as Ada poured.

"You wish you were back in the Army, don't you, Hobart?" His sister always seem to know what was on his mind.

"I don't know … perhaps. I certainly don't want to disappoint you and Jarvis, but …"

"What would you do?"

"Sam Tanner thinks I should join him in the Navy. To be honest, that thought is appealing. I just don't know."

Marie, their housekeeper, came to the porch.

126

"Mrs. Adams, you've a visitor. A young woman. "

"Did she give her name, Marie?"

"I believe she said Miss Oakley, ma'am."

"Oh, very well, Marie – please show her in."

Marie bobbed and left. Ada turned to Hobart.

"Miss Helen Oakley. I know her through church, and I believe she has been carrying on a rather intense correspondence with our serious younger brother." Her eyes twinkled.

"Jerome? Jerome the student is courting? Oh, I must meet this damsel who has stolen that young man's heart."

Hobart stood up as a young woman with striking dark eyes stepped onto the porch. He was preparing to say something flippant about his brother but stopped. The girl was wearing a plain black dress, and its meaning was clear. She was in mourning.

Ada rose and the two women embraced.

"Mrs. Adams, I thank you so kindly for the note of sympathy. The family is grateful for your concern."

"Oh, my dear, we're just so, sad for you all." She paused. "May I introduce my brother Hobart? Hobart, may I present Miss Helen Oakley?"

Hobart inclined his head to precisely the appropriate degree. The girl bowed slightly and said "Mr. Walker, it is a pleasure."

He pulled back a chair from the table. "Miss Oakley, would you care to join us? May I pour you some lemonade against the heat?"

"Thank you much, sir, that would be kind."

Ada turned to Hobart. "Miss Oakley mourns the death of her brother, Lieutenant Alexander Varian. He was, I believe, in the First Regiment, Ohio Volunteer Infantry. Is that correct, my dear?"

"Yes, indeed, Company D. He was wounded in Dalton, Georgia and taken to the hospital in Chattanooga. At first we thought, though wounded severely, he would recover, but he was shot in the chest and expired two weeks later."

"I am deeply sorry, Miss Oakley. Please do accept my condolences. "

She nodded.

"Hobart has just returned from Washington. He was with the One Hundred-Fiftieth Ohio Volunteers."

The girl looked up. "Oh, that's wonderful that you would serve our country so."

Ada continued – "He also served in the cavalry and in the 44th New York Infantry. He was with General McClellan in the Peninsula Campaign."

By this time Hobart was shaking his head at his sister.

This isn't the time to start talking about wounds.

Ada nodded her understanding, and tried to shift the topic.

"So, what have you heard from Jerome?"

"Yes, indeed, Miss Oakley, whatever would that grave young medical student have to say to such a belle?"

Ada's eyebrows arched, but Miss Oakley didn't seem to notice.

"Oh," she chirped, "Jerome is such a dear. He was sadly taken with Aleck's death, - they were quite friendly - and has said he wants to enlist to, as he put it, 'take his place'."

This time Hobart's eyebrows shot up. "Jerome? Enlist?"

"Indeed, he wrote that he would enlist and sign up for the V. T. Sharpshooters. He waits only for his father's consent."

"Which, I fear, he is unlikely to receive. I don't mean to be brusque, Miss Oakley, but I do not feel our father would be keen to see another son enlist. However, Jerome's a strong fellow. He's quiet, but he's strong. I'd admire to listen in on their conversation!"

After a few moments of conversation, the young woman arose.

"I'm off to visit Mrs. Starkey and some of the boys in the hospital. Please do give my regards to Mr. Adams."

"I shall, indeed, Miss Oakley. Our best to all your family."

After she left, Hobart shot his sister a quizzical grin. "Is this a serious thing, Ada? I've never thought Jerome to be the flirtatious type."

"I'm not sure. He visited here some time ago and they met. They've been writing regularly since then. You're not the only one in the family to grow up, you know."

"Evidently not. This will bear some watching."

*   *   *

By the time September arrived, he made up his mind.

"I am going to New York and meet up with Sam," he told Ada. "I'll have to explain this – again – to Father and Mother, but I believe it is what I am meant to do."

Ada nodded.

*   *   *

Once more, he rode the train into New Jersey, and took the ferry across to New York and then to Brooklyn. He felt nothing like the nineteen-year-old who had paraded so proudly to the fields of Virginia. In fact, those days seemed like an entirely different lifetime. Still, Ferdinand and Elmira were delighted to see him when he strode through the door on Clinton Avenue. After only a few days, though, his restlessness resurfaced.

His father saw it right away.

"Son, there is something troubling you. Would you like to walk?"

Together, they walked the familiar Brooklyn streets.

"Father, I'm not at all certain just what I should be doing. I thought perhaps I'd join Sam Tanner in the Navy, but now that doesn't seem so inviting. The war seems to be going our way, and could well be over before too much longer, but there is a part of me that still feels I should be in the field."

"You're a grown man now, Hobart. You might have been a bit of a boy when you left, but you've lived some hard lessons since then. It is no secret that your mother and I would prefer to see you safe and away from the fighting, but we also know where your heart is. You are a bright young man, son, and I am comfortable you will make a good decision."

As they walked back into the house, George, now a strapping teen, met them in the foyer.

"Uncle Jesse is here," he said.

Elmira's brother Jesse was a well established figure in Brooklyn, and much loved by all his nephews and nieces. Hobart walked into the sitting room, a broad smile warming his face, and his uncle stood.

"Come, Nephew, let's have a look at you. You don't look much the wear for your adventures. In fact, you've grown into quite the man. You're well?"

"Quite well, Uncle, and I thank you. You do, as well."

The older man laughed aloud.

"This old warhorse is one step away from the pasture, I think. Still, he gets about a bit."

After dinner, the men sat in the parlor and talked well into the evening. They chatted about the Peninsula Campaign, about Jubal Early and the Shenandoah, and Gettysburg. Elmira kissed her brother on his weathered cheek and went up the stairs to bed, and the younger Walkers followed her soon afterward, leaving only Ferdinand, Jesse and Hobart. Finally Jesse faced Hobart.

"What is it you'd like, Nephew?"

"Uncle, I think I'd like to try another go." Ferdinand stiffened, and the other two sensed it. Jesse chewed on the stub of his pipe, silent. After a long, awkward pause, he spoke, almost to himself.

"I'm not sure you'd want to be in the 139th – it might not look too good for me to have my nephew in my own unit. I do have some friends, though, and perhaps we could find a suitable place in one of the others. Let me nose around a bit, would you?"

He rose, shook Ferdinand's hand, patted Hobart on the shoulder, and walked into the autumn night.

A day or so later, a young soldier in uniform knocked on the door.

"Message for Mr. Hobart Walker. It's from General Smith, sir."

Hobart tore open the envelope and scanned the lines of neat writing. A faint smile played around his lips, and he folded the paper, tucking it into his pocket.

"Anything you'd care to share with us, son?" He started, not realizing his mother had been standing beside him all the while.

"There might be an answer here, mother. May we speak when father returns?"

That evening, he sat with his parents, who looked on anxiously.

"Uncle Jesse suggests what might be the right solution. He writes that he can get me into another regiment – the Hundred and Sixth New York. I'd have to go up to Goshen to enlist, but they'll take me right away, and there's bounty money to be had, too. Best of all, he says that he can arrange for me to be sent to Hart Island, near Pelham, on Detached Duty there. It is a Draft Rendezvous, and they train recruits. I'd be there and could come home regularly. The rest of the regiment is near Petersburgh, but I would be permanent party, unless I wanted to go back into the field at some point."

His parents looked at each other. For the first time, he saw the lines on both their faces. He realized that the war had taken a toll on them, too. At last Ferdinand spoke.

"If you'd be happy with that, son, I think we'd see it as a worthy compromise. You would come here often, would you not?"

"I would, indeed, father. You might well be tired of the sight of me!"

The trunk he'd packed before leaving Cleveland was still in transit, so when Hobart reported to Hart Island, the Quartermaster provided a new uniform issue. He smiled, thinking that, once the trunk arrived, he'd have three blue sack coats - a four-button issue and one of the New York special eight buttoned coat on the way - and three pairs of light-blue woolen trousers. The new kepi the sergeant handed him just did not seem to sit comfortably, and he knew that once it got to New York, he'd quietly replace it with his original, "lucky", cap. In the clothing that seemed second-nature to him, it was if he had never left. It didn't even concern him that he was once again a private, having been both a Sergeant and a Lieutenant.

As quickly as he became comfortable with the Hart Island routine, he wrote Ferdinand.

Head Quarters
Draft Rendezvous
Hart Island
Oct 9th 64

My Dear Father,

I saw Uncle Jesse yesterday, and I gave him my address, you can come over to the island to see me by going to General Dix and get a pass. I wish George would come over and bring my watch & writing materials, no matter about my boots at present. Did you get the $475 I sent you?

I am now detailed in Co. C, 1st Battalion doing Guard duty & if I wished it I could probably remain here the rest of my time, but would have no chance of promotion & would prefer to go to the Regiment.

We are to have 15,000 Rebel prisoners here soon.

Tell George to tell the Dillers if he sees them that am on the Island.

Hart Island is a fine place & would well repay a trip even of itself.

Your son
Hobart

P. S. If you will pay for fixing my watch I will give it to him when he comes here.

*　　*　　*

Not long after he arrived, his youngest brother George arrived to spend a Sunday, glad to be with his brother. Hobart enjoyed escorting him around the island.

"I'm a guard and a troop escort."

"Escort?"

"Yes. Many of these fellows collect a bounty when they enlist. Most are honorable, but some will desert at the first chance, and escape with the money. They are good on the Island, but once they leave, we can lose a few. Now they send them in groups to their regiments, and we send along an officer and several soldiers to keep an eye on 'em."

"Where do they go?"

"Most of them go to General Sherman's army."

"In Atlanta?"

"Down that way. I don't but feel he'll be moving on from that soon, though. We take people to Hilton Head in South Carolina …"

"Where it all began," observed George.

Hobart nodded and continued "… and they meet up with their units from there. Then we come back here, I visit you in Brooklyn, and begin all over again."

"Do you like that better than being in the field?"

He paused. "I don't know, George. It's safer here, certainly, but there was just something about being out there …"

"You could get hurt, though."

"I did, remember?" They both laughed.

"We'll see how things go this year. It might be over before too much longer. "

"What will you do then?"

Hobart shrugged.

* * *

Walking across the parade ground one cold November morning, his overcoat pulled tightly against the relentless wind, he passed another soldier, walking the other way. Something about the man seemed familiar, and he slowed his pace. Stopping, he turned around, to see that the other man, too, had stopped and was looking back at him. For a moment, they looked at each other, then recognition dawned.

"John?" Hobart called out. "John Wust? That you?"

The two men closed the distance between them and grasping each others' hand, laughed aloud. "Walker? I thought that might be you, but you were a Sergeant last I saw you."

Hobart nodded. "Things have a funny way of turning out, don't they?" The cold forgotten, the two veterans of Belle Isle stood on the windswept parade field to reminisce.

"Where you been?"

"Doin' all right?"

"Have you seen…?"

As they conversed in the code known only to veteran soldiers, Hobart could see more than a few streaks of gray in his friend's full beard. Recalling that John was older than most of the men who enlisted, Hobart saw that the experiences of the war had taken something of a toll.

Wonder what I look like to him.

With promises to stay in contact, the men clapped each other's shoulders one final time and separated, each going his own way.

* * *

"They're bringing in prisoners" Word got around the barracks.

"Do you know that, or is just Madam Rumor, again"

"Pretty certain. They began clearing some of the barracks at the south end, and some of the fellows have been put to work, settin' up a fence."

Huh. Gone from being a prisoner to guarding 'em. On an island, too.

Looking west to City Island or east to Sands Point on Long Island, he thought frequently of the foaming waters of the James, the barrier between him and freedom during what seemed a distant lifetime.

Better chance of escaping Belle Isle than the East River.

* * *

"Happy New Year, son"

"Happy New Year, Father. Let us hope this will be a good one."

They walked along Clinton Avenue, the January wind whipping viciously around them. Leaves and bits of paper danced along the gutters and the corners, where street vendors hawked their treats, were vacant. "No oysters today, I'm afraid."

"You're not still thinking about the Navy, are you?"

"I don't believe so, Father. The newspaper said this morning that there are fifty vessels within sight of Wilmington. Fifty! The city cannot stand much longer. When it falls, there goes the last major port, so the blockade runners will have no haven. Without blockade runners, there isn't much for the Navy to do. I trust I would be better off just staying here until the war ends. "

"Which I pray will be soon!"

"I should think it would. When we took the Mississippi, we cut the Confederacy in half. Now that General Sherman is in Savannah, it's been quartered. General Sheridan is in the Shenandoah, and General Grant is at Petersburg. There isn't much that General Lee can do – no place to go. We're squeezing him from all sides."

"The sooner the blood stops, the better for all of us." Hobart nodded and they continued their walk, bundled tightly against the cold.

* * *

The Walker household was much quieter. With Ada in Cleveland, Jerome serving as a Field Agent in the Sanitary Commission in Virginia and Hobart at Hart Island, only George remained at home. Emma, a vivacious teenager, had gone to stay with Ada and Jarvis in Cleveland. A heavy, wet snow fell on New York City. Hobart dipped his pen into the inkwell and wrote -

Brooklyn, Feb 5, 65

Dear Sister Emma

I have not forgotten, if I have neglected you, but I have lately been so much on the move that I have written to no one for long time, but trusted to the folks at home to keep my friends that care to know of me posted as to my whereabouts. I have been twice to Hilton Head & Beaufort, South Carolina and once to Harpers Ferry since I last wrote to you; each time I have been home on my return, this time I have been here a week and go back to the Island tomorrow.

I was very much surprised on my arrival here last week to see Kate. She is working hard and seems to be feeling well and contented.

Uncle A. W. started to-night for Virginia to visit Uncle Henric he will be gone about two weeks. Aunt Eliza has had another extra nervous spell and has had Dr. Newcomb two or three times but is now some better.

I suppose Jarvis heard of me lately through Capt. Wilson he came from Hilton Head on the same boat with me. Oh, how sick I was going down to Hilton Head this last time. It is the first time I ever was Sea Sick and I hope it will be the last, the weather was very rough. I could stand on the decks of the vessel and see the waves all around us as high as our masts and the next moment look over the sides of the ship into the water so far below that it would seem impossible to get down there without swamping. There were a great many "colored gentlemen" on board, and it was almost ridiculous to hear them pray. They blocked up the stairs and the deck and if you spoke to them the only response would be "we's gwine to sink. Oh, Lord save this poor niggah and bring him safe out of this and I will never come to sea again."

Has Ada heard from Jerome lately, Mother heard quite often, he seems well contented and has already saved $100.

Direct as before to Hart Island, & write soon to

Your affectionate Brother,
Hobart

Jack wishes to be Remembered.

*   *   *

Slightly more than a week after he'd written Emma, the newspapers trumpeted the story that both Wilmington and Charleston had fallen. He'd made the right choice, and resolved to finish the war in his current assignment.

In mid-March, as the first hints of spring began to push through the harsh winds and freezing sleet pounding in off Long Island Sound, he was called once again to the company office. He entered the office and saluted smartly.

Captain Bullock, the company commander, looked up from his desk and smiled, slightly. "Two things for you. First, congratulations – you're now a Corporal. Best get some stripes. Secondly, get your traps together. We have another lot to take to the field."

Hobart relaxed and returned the grin. 'And whereabouts might we be headed this time, sir?"

The officer looked back down to his desk and scanned several pages there. "Wilmington, North Carolina, ever been there?" Hobart shook his head.

"Well, this will be new for us both. Me, the Lieutenant, Sergeant Edwards, and twenty of you lads are taking a troop that will join General Sherman. Just in time to win the war."

"When do we leave?"

"Looks like we'll be moving out on Wednesday. The twenty-second," he replied.

Hobart saluted again, executed a crisp "About face" and left the office. Time to pack.

Quickly he pulled together what he thought he'd need on a reasonably short trip and packed it into his knapsack. He toyed with the idea of bringing his heavy overcoat with the cape across the shoulders. It was still winter in New York, but he thought that it would be warmer by the time they reached the Carolinas and decided not to add it to the pile. When he was finished, he looked for pen and paper, intending to write his father. Before he began to write he sat back, chewing absently on the end of the pen. It would be a short trip, he thought, and there really hadn't been much to write about since the last time he was in Brooklyn, so he put the pen aside.

I'll write when I get back

"Pack only what you need in the field! Everything else gets boxed up and you can ship it home. You'll be travelling light out there, and you don't want Johnny Reb to get his hands on your goods!"

"Lieutenant, take the escort party to the Quartermaster and check out rifles."

"Yes, sir! You heard him, boys, over to the Q-M!"

In columns of four, recruits in front and escorts behind, they left the camp, along the short path to the docks on the west side of the island.

"There's your ride! On board, now – watch you don't fall in. Can't fight the Secesh if you're soaking wet!"

Down the East River, enroute the docks on the west side of Manhattan. Passing the Navy base at Wallabout, Hobart glanced up at the reassuring slopes of the hill at Washington Park. It had become a bit of a ritual on these trips, and he tipped his kepi slightly as they passed.

The little convoy eased out of the center channel and closer to the New York side, making a graceful turn around Battery Park and another one, slightly to starboard, as they headed up the Hudson River. At Pier 17 the tug turned sharply into the island, the barges swinging wide behind it. They came up against the dock, while sailors on both barges threw mooring lines to their colleagues on the pier. In a moment they were secured and the escorting soldiers scrambled first out of the barges and onto the dock. Behind them came the recruits, passing between two lines of veterans across to the vessel that lay there, moored tightly. Hobart read the name on the squat superstructure – General Lyon.

Several of the soldiers from the escort party leaned against the rail as they edged toward the dock.

"That it?"

"Yup. General Lyon. New ship, I hear."

"Built here?"

"No, Connecticut, they say. Launched last year and already has a couple of trips to Wilmington."

"Well, one ship's pretty much like another. Gets us there, gets us home – that's all that matters."

Heads bobbed in unison.

There it sat, at the pier, ready to sail again. The deck was mostly flush, with only a small, stubby superstructure breaking the line from side to side. Forward, at the bow, a low triangular structure suggested some shelter, and a smaller construction stood atop it. Two tall masts and a funnel indicated that it had the capability to use both sails and steam as propulsion. A tendril of sooty smoke eddied up from the stack. The ship had fires under the boilers and was ready to go to sea.

As quickly as the new soldiers could be counted and recounted and ushered below, John Haydon, the First Mate and a seasoned mariner, strode along the deck, his gaze focused on the lines that ran tautly from the ship to the bollards on the pier.

"Let go the spring lines!" he barked. Immediately two hemp ropes were slipped from the bollards and fell into the water. Hands on the ship pulled them expertly aboard and coiled them, dripping wet.

"Let go the bow line!" and the line holding the ship's bow to the pier slid into the water. Haydon turned and waved to the pilot house. The lazy wisp of smoke from the funnel thickened into a torrent, and the water at the stern of the ship began to froth. The bow edged away from the pier and the space widened.

He turned toward the stern and bellowed "Let go aft!" The last line dropped into the water. The General Lyon moved slowly forward into the Hudson. They were underway, enroute Fortress Monroe and, ultimately, North Carolina.

Though not a sailor, Hobart knew that March can be a deceptive month in the North Atlantic. Winter storms are still possible, whipping the water into crashing waves and making a voyage miserable. This time, however, the seas were smooth, the winds favorable, and the ship moved steadily south.

*   *   *

Hobart leaned against the rail, deep in thought. The propellers in the stern beat a quietly steady tattoo against the sea, and the wires hummed in the breeze. His mind bounced from Buffalo to Belle Isle, from Clara to Cleveland. He was so immersed in his reverie that he didn't see the young soldier who moved up next to him, leaning against the railing. Hobart twitched slightly when he finally noticed him.

"Sorry," said the boy. "I didn't mean to startle you."

"That's all right – just thinking."

The youth was silent for a moment, then began to speak softly. "Do you think we'll see action?"

"Can't say, for sure. I think it's probable, though. Lots of fight left in the Rebs. They're sturdy fellows, and most of them are veterans. They've been there, they've seen the elephant, and they know what they're doing. You be careful down there. Listen to your Sergeants. "

The boy nodded.

"Can I ask you a question?"

"Of course. What is it?"

"Some of the boys are saying that they're not going to fight. They're saying that as soon as we get there, they're going to desert. They say they'll slip away, or jump over the side when we get close to shore and swim away. Do people do that?"

Hobart swing around, and faced him. He looked fully into the younger man's eyes and spoke.

"Listen to me and listen very carefully. They send us along to be sure you get to your regiments. They need you and they are counting on you. People try to light out from time to time, but mostly they don't get there. If they do, and they get caught, there's a court martial, they line them up, and they shoot them."

The boy blanched. "Do they really shoot them?"

Hobart nodded, his face set and grim. "They do, and don't think anything about it. Let me tell you something else. A couple of months ago, we were on our way to Hilton Head, down in South Carolina. We were pretty close to the shore and we heard a splash. Two of the privates did just that, they jumped over the side and were swimming toward the shore."

He paused. The boy stared at him.

"What happened?"

"We shot them. Shot them both. Right there in the water."

The youngster gulped so loudly Hobart could hear it.

"Did … did you shoot them?"

"They were shot before I got there. If I'd been there, I would have, though. Absolutely."

"What happened to the bodies?"

"Who knows? They were floating in the water and we never even slowed down."

There was a long, long silence. The propellers thrashed astern, but there was little other sound. Finally, timidly, the boy spoke again.

"Corporal, they say you've been in the army since the beginning. Since it began. Is that true?"

"Well, not every day, but pretty much."

"They say you were shot, and that you were a prisoner in Richmond. Are they making that up?" More confident, he pressed his questions.

"Yes, that is true. I was wounded at Yorktown and at Malvern Hill, and they had me at Libby and Belle Isle. I got paroled after that."

"Why did you come back? You could have stayed out and done anything. Why did you keep enlisting?"

Hobart looked up at the clouds scudding by, soft white blossoms on a pasture of blue. He thought.

Why did I?

At last he spoke, almost to himself.

"I think … I think that I … and the other fellows … just want to get this done. Everyone wants it to end, for the killing to end, for the cannon to stop, but I think we just want to be sure it's over, and that this is one country again. Everything else can be worked out, be we want to see it to the finish."

The boy was silent, staring at the water swirling past. Finally he looked up, nodded, and without a word, left and went below.

*   *   *

The rest of the trip from New York to Norfolk passed quietly. The waves didn't move the ship enough to make it uncomfortable for the soldiers, most of whom were at sea for the first time. They were excited the morning they made the wide turn between Cape Charles and Cape Henry, entering Hampton Roads and dropping anchor near Fortress Monroe.

Hobart watched as a boat went ashore long enough to see if there were any messages for them. He leaned against the rail and gazed at the Virginia shore.

Wasn't all that long ago the Forty-Fourth landed. Seems like another life.

He glanced up only when the boat returned. Word drifted around that they would stay overnight and leave for Wilmington the following day.

It dawned sunny and mild, and the crew wasted no time in hauling in the anchor and getting underway. The Lyon glided along the channel and turned south, into the Atlantic. The soldiers watched in fascination as dolphins, in groups of two and three, followed effortlessly alongside, leaping elegantly out of the water and diving beneath the hull. As they made the turn, Hobart pointed to a tall structure ashore.

"Do you see that?" he asked a young New York soldier. The boy nodded.

"Cape Henry Lighthouse," Hobart declared knowingly. "First construction project in this country's history," he added. The soldier gazed, wide-eyed. "It was?" "Yep, made with the same stone as the White House." The new man marveled at this knowledgeable veteran.

Like the trip from New York, the sea was kind for the two days it took to get from Norfolk to the southern tip of North Carolina. The ocean picked up as they passed Cape Hatteras. Again, Hobart regaled a group of listeners. "Graveyard of the Atlantic," he intoned. "Many, many a ship has gone down there." The men were silent.

As the sky lightened the next morning, they arrived at the mouth of the Cape Fear River. There was a conversation ongoing among the officers, as they gathered around the wheel. Hobart couldn't make out what they were saying, but he could see them gesturing emphatically. He edged closer to the group, trying to remain inconspicuous. When he could hear them, he stopped and pretended to look out over the railing.

"It's too shallow, Captain!" said one man, pounding his fist into the palm of his hand.

"Seven, mebbe eight feet, and that's if we read the tide right." Another protested.

"Plenty of water to get through. If we go the other way, it will add a full day. We can do it!"

After several minutes of discussion, the First Mate stepped in. "Captain," he said, "If we stay close aboard that buoy," and he pointed to a wooden object bobbing in the water, "and then the next one, we come west-sou'-west and we can be the river channel. I've got leadsmen in the bows, and we can drop anchor if it shoals too sharp."

The captain thought a minute and nodded. "We'll go this way. Set the leadsmen." The ship began to edge forward again. In the front, soldiers watched with interest as sailors on each side twirled long lines with lead weights and periodically flung them in long, graceful arcs ahead of the ship. Hauling the lines in, they noted the intervals marked with bits of cloth and called out numbers. Others repeated them back to the captain, standing alongside the helmsman at the wheel.

"By the mark nine! By the mark eight!" The man on the starboard side spun his and called back

"By the mark thirteen!" Haydon stabbed the chart with a forefinger and said "That's that hole, right alongside the buoy!"

Soldiers crowded both sides of the ship, as a low, sandy shore appeared before them. When they seemed uncomfortably close to the shore, the captain called out "Come left! Steer two six zero!"

The helmsman spun the big wooden wheel and slowly the ship turned to the left. Now a low, narrow island appeared ahead and to their left. "Zeek Island," muttered the mate.

The captain nodded. The leadsmen continued their chant. Slowly the island passed on their left, and the mate pointed out another buoy, ahead and on their right. "Number Six," he said. "Come right! Steer Zero one zero!"

Slowly, ponderously, the bow of the General Lyon crept to the right. The song of the leadsman began to change. "By the mark ten! By the mark thirteen! By the mark fifteen!" They had cleared the islands and come into the deeper channel of the Cape Fear River.

Wilmington lay miles ahead of them, and they were still in a precarious channel, but they were past the shoals. The captain turned to the mate. "That was a bit close, Mister Haydon. I believe we'll take the southern channel when we leave." The mate didn't argue.

As they crept up the river, Hobart leaned against the rail, watching the shoreline pass by. A man came up beside him, a man he knew as William Brown, a cook on board. They had been nodding acquaintances, and Hobart turned to him with a question –

"William, did you notice anything different about coming into this port? Something different from the others?"

"No, not especially. Why, did you?"

"I don't know. I remember we stopped going into New York last time to pick up a pilot, and stopped to let him off when we left. Same thing in Hilton Head and Norfolk. But no pilot here. I wonder why?"

"Can't imagine. Wait, there's Mr. Gibbs. He's First Officer, he should know. Ahoy! Mr. Gibbs!"

The officer came over to the rail. "What can I do for you?"

"Mr. Gibbs, Corporal Walker wanted to know if we took a pilot on board. Did we?"

"Not here, boys, not now. All the locals who know the river enough to pilot have been hand-in-glove with the blockade runners. No, a man would be off his chump to admit to knowing the river. They'd have him in irons right away. We're on our own here."

The ship proceeded cautiously north, keeping to the center of the narrow channel and sounding the depths regularly. The variety of Federal warships still in the river excited the new soldiers, who crowded the rails, staring at the ships and chattering.

Hobart noticed a trim, three-masted gunboat among them. It looked more like yacht than a man-of-war, but the cannon mounted on its deck meant that its presence on the Cape Fear was not a pleasure cruise. Gold letters on its stern proclaimed this to be the Shawmut. He was admiring the ship as they passed close aboard, when a young naval officer appeared on deck. The sailor looked up as the transport glided past, the passengers crowding the rails and gawking. He saw a corporal standing slightly apart from the others and, as their eyes met, the soldier spontaneously waved. The officer smiled slightly and waved back.

"Who's that, Hobart?"

"I've no idea. It just came over me to wave."

On the warship, a man asked the officer: "Commander Walker, do you know who that soldier is?"

"No, just saying hello."

*   *   *

They continued up the river, inching along. As the ship's boilers panted steam, the ship's crew manned the leadsmen positions. When at last they reached Wilmington, everyone was exhausted. The ship slowed to a halt midstream, the bow facing north and the piers forty yards away.

Hobart watched this evolution with interest, curious to see what would happen next. Behind him he heard a stern voice command "Let go the anchor!". The heavy anchor dropped away from the ship, chain rattling through the guide and into the mud of the river bottom. After a minute or so of the ear-shattering noise, the captain waved his arm and a seaman spun the capstan brake wheel, stopping the chain. For a moment it appeared that the ship would remain in the middle of the channel, until a small boat arrived alongside.

Crewmen on the General Lyon tossed a light line tied to the heavy mooring hawser to a boy in the boat. He hauled it in and rowed it to the pier. There, another boy dexterously wrapped it in a figure-eight around a cleat and the ship was secured. Without command, a group of seven or eight sailors on the Lyon picked up the line lying on the deck and wrapped it around a capstan. Leaning into the spokes of the wheel, the sailors hauled the hawser tight. The slack came up out of the water and, after several additional pulls, the bow slowly began to turn toward the shore. Looking aft, Hobart could see another party of sailors performing a similar maneuver there, and the ship inched closer to the river bank. Finally, it was alongside the pier, leaving the anchor and a hundred yards or more of anchor chain on the river bottom. When lines at the bow, stern and amidships were tautly tied and secure, a wooden gangway was run from the pier onto the deck of the ship.

Captain Bullock lined up the recruits from Hart Island and marched them down the brow. On the pier, they formed columns and with a squad of escorts in front and one behind marched off the pier, up the river road, headed for the Union lines. The march did not last long, and it was still early when they arrived at the picket lines.

"Captain Bullock, Draft Rendezvous Hart Island. Where is Forty-Seventh New York Infantry?"

The sentry waved an arm. "Half mile up that road, Cap'n. You bringin' us fresh-uns?"

The escort party stood off to the side as the new soldiers were counted off. Without looking back, they trudged up the road, toward the line.

Captain Bullock turned back to them. "All right, men. Route march back to Wilmington. We'll have six hours liberty, then you need to be back aboard the ship. They're loading an Illinois regiment and some others, but I was told we would be leaving on the flood tide. Let's go."

With practiced ease, the soldiers stacked their arms next to the brow. Captain Bullock posted a sentry to guard them and released the others. Long lines of people, soldiers and civilians, stood on the pier, waiting to board the General Lyon for the return trip. Hobart and the others chatted briefly with some of the men in uniform.

"What unit?"

"Fifty-Sixth Illinois. Done three years, heading back to Springfield to muster out. You?" It was what had become a standard script among military men meeting for the first time. After a while, Hobart left the others and wandered off.

The wooden pier on the east side of the river ran for several hundred yards, then became a dirt trail alongside the water. He strolled casually along, aware of something out of the ordinary, but unable to put his finger on what it might be. He looked at his pocket watch and saw that it was close to noon, and suddenly it occurred to him.

Silence.

The quiet was unnerving for a town this size in the middle of the day. There was the lonely echo of horse hooves on stone streets, but little else besides the chirping of the birds. There were few people walking along the streets and the ones there did so in silence, most with their heads down. No one looked up, no one spoke, no one smiled. At high noon, a time when church bells should be ringing in an enthusiastic symphony, it was still.

Steep bluffs rose sharply from the river's edge, bedecked with spring foliage. Redbud trees exploded in lavender bursts while, deeper in the shade, dogwood proffered their white blossoms from gnarled and twisted limbs. Absent-mindedly, Hobart plucked a blossom as he wandered along. The four heart-shaped petals, with a red spot at the end, were a favorite of his mother.

> There's a legend, children. They say that Christ's cross was made of dogwood. In those days it was straight and strong. After the Crucifixion, God cursed the tree, saying it would always be crooked and bent, and good for nothing. But God is kind, too, and gave the dogwood something else. The bloom, He said, would always be a reminder of the day on Calvary – four petals, each tipped in red – the head, the hands and the feet of the Savior. That's the legend of the dogwood.

Hobart looked at the flower in his hand.

Hmm. Maybe this is my new beginning. It'll be Easter in a couple of weeks. I'll have to ask Mother.

* * *

Wilmington is a attractive town, he thought, although it showed the effects of four years' conflict. The stately homes, for all their classic lines, needed some work.

They haven't seen paint in a while.

Gardens that looked as if they should be bursting with flowers had dull, ordinary rows of vegetables. Still, he felt, there was substance to this village. Looking up the slopes to the homes and churches above, Hobart was again taken back to the bluffs in Brooklyn, and suddenly experienced an unusual pang of nostalgia. He was ready to go home.

The General Lyon was scheduled to sail on the flowing tide, and Hobart glanced at the water. He couldn't tell if the ripples and eddies meant the tide was ebbing or flowing and decided not to risk being left behind. Reaching the dock, he saw lines of passengers still waiting to board, and he guessed it would be an hour or so before they got underway. He turned up a narrow street leading away from the dockside and continued his exploration. There were shops and stores, almost all of them closed and shuttered. Walking the deserted streets, it was if the buildings were faces, their vacant windows eyes narrowed in fury and their locked doors mouths pursed shut in anger and shame.

Invader, the empty windows glared, and the barred and bolted doors whispered back with scorn – *Yankee.*

He shrugged and continued along, on a meandering ramble, looping around to the footpath leading back to the pier.

As he walked along the street, he heard a voice, rhythmically chanting. As he drew closer, the words amazed him:

Here's your fine salty oysters!
Fine fresh oysters
Just out of the boat,
Buy a few hundred
They're an excellent lot!

Hobart stopped short and sagged against the dusty brick building. He shook his head, trying to clear the thoughts that jumbled against each other like marbles in a sack. He closed his eyes.

* * *

Brooklyn, April 1858

He walked with his father as he often did at the end of the day. In the streets of Brooklyn, they passed pushcart vendors hawking their wares with distinctive, often poetic cries. Hobart knew that his father was especially drawn to a little boy, sovereign of his corner kingdom at Flushing Avenue and Kent Street. He had a basket filled with clams and oysters, covered with a thick layer of wet seaweed. Alongside he had a tin, filled with hot coals, on which a formation of the bivalves sizzled.

As people passed, he would chant in his thin, little boy voice:
Here's your fine Rockaway oysters! Here they G-O!
Fine Rockaway oysters
Just out of the boat,
Buy a few hundred
They're an excellent lot!
Ferdinand liked to stop and act as if he was considering a important purchase.

"They look delightful today. What is the price?"

"Two for a penny, sir, special to a fine gentleman such as yourself!"

Ferdinand pretended to ponder, then turned to Hobart.

"What say you, son? Would an oyster or two spoil your supper?"

Hobart loved the sweet, salty treats and emphatically shook his head.

"Well, then, perhaps just a half-dozen … freshly cooked."

The urchin took six large oysters off the coals, placed them in a sheet of paper and handed them over. "Three cents, if you please."

Ferdinand rummaged through his change purse, withdrew a half-dime.

"This seems to be the smallest I have, but it will have to do. "

The boy nodded his thanks.

*   *   *

Hobart squeezed his eyes tightly, the memory fading.

There, squatting against a brick building that faced the river, a man sat. A black man, white hair, face and hands lined by decades of back-breaking labor, head bowed as if he was speaking to the ground. Next to him was a battered iron pot, filled with coals. Arrayed on the coals was a formation of oysters – large oysters – sputtering in the heat. It was as if he'd been plucked off the sidewalk at Flushing Avenue and deposited hundreds of miles away.

Oysters!

Though his accent was certainly different from that of Brooklyn, Hobart was astonished that the chant was practically identical. He stopped.

"How much?"

The man raised his head, slightly, and looked cautiously up at the soldier. "Three of 'em for a penny, suh."

Hobart dug into his pocket and felt several coins. "I'll have six, please." The man nodded and deftly picked a half-dozen from the goals, placing them on a crumpled piece of newsprint.

He held them out. Hobart looked at the change in his hand and selected a half-dime, extending it. The man took it, looked at both sides.

"I ain't got any pennies, suh." Hobart smiled slightly. The tableau seemed surreal, and he could almost feel Ferdinand standing alongside him.

"Then it will just have to do." The faintest ghost of a smile crossed the man's furrowed features. He nodded, almost imperceptibly. "Thank you, suh" he whispered.

*   *   *

Savoring every bite, he sauntered back to the ship. There were only a few people waiting to board, and he could see sailors swarming the main deck, making preparations for getting underway. Joining the rest of the escort party waiting at the brow, he retrieved his rifle and, almost the last in line, boarded.

Men on the pier pulled the gangway away from the side of the ship, and let go the two spring lines, into the water. The stack belched a swirl of grimy smoke, and the captain called

"Let go the bow line!"

Ropes fell into the muddy water with a splash.

"Hoist the anchor!"

Sailors gathered around a capstan in the bow began their laborious circular dance. Slowly the anchor chain came up out of the muck and snaked into the chain locker below.

The bow of the General Lyon pulled away from the pier, until it pointed straight out into the river, toward the rice beds on the western shore. One of the mates, standing in the bow, watched the anchor chain intently, and as the anchor itself appeared, called out "Anchor's aweigh!" Immediately the captain called "Let go the stern line!" and it dropped into the water.

Strong hands pulled it aboard as the helmsman leaned hard into the wheel, spinning it rapidly. With the propeller churning the water into a coffee-colored froth behind, the Lyon turned slowly, ponderously, until it was headed south, down the Cape Fear and toward the sea.

*   *   *

The trip from Wilmington to the open sea took several hours. Hobart and the others leaned against the railing, watching the North Carolina countryside pass by. They passed the still-smoldering wreckage of Confederate fortifications.

"What's the one?"

"Used to be Fort Anderson."

"What the hell is that thing?" A blue-clad arm stretched out toward something in the river – something none of them had ever seen before.

"That's a Quaker." A sailor walking by overheard the question and chuckled.

"A Quaker? I don't get it."

The bluejacket stopped and put his forearms on the railing. "They built that thing out of wood and canvas, and put a couple of logs in it to look like cannon." Hobart remembered the Rebel fort at Centreville and nodded appreciatively. The sailor continued –

"Rebs thought it was a monitor and wasted a lot of power and shot on it. They must have wondered why it never fired back, but it worked like a charm. Fellows called it a 'Quaker' on account of it would not or could not fight."

The soldiers snickered. After several tedious hours, the ship reached the mouth of the river and came left, headed into the waters of the Atlantic. They passed the last, small smudge of land. A passing sailor nodded toward it. "Smith Island," he said. "We're at sea now."

I'll need to be sure to tell Mother the Secesh have named an island after her family.

The Lyon cleared shoal water and the Captain chose to anchor overnight. Early the next morning, they weighed anchor again and, with engine and sail, set a course that would take them past Cape Hatteras and back to the harbor at Norfolk. As they reached unprotected water, the ship took on a regular, if unpronounced roll. Hobart saw several of the sailors tying lines around loose objects on deck and tightening ropes already secured.

"What's doin', boys? Seems like everyone's all fired busy!"

A sailor looked up at him. "Captain says the glass has been dropping through the night, and he opines there's a blow comin' in. If it's from the west, we'll just roll with it. If it's a n'or-easter … they can get a bit rambunctious. It happens this time of year, and he wants everything to be snug as a bug, if it does." He returned to his tasks.

Throughout the day, the weather deteriorated. The wind began to blow harder, and the waves went from ripples on the surface to rhythmic surf, growing in size and frequency. The ship, heading northeast began to feel the impact on the starboard bow, a combination of pitch and yaw, making the decks extremely unsteady, and turning more than one inexperienced face green. The waves also pushed the ship west of its course – closer to the pounding breakers along the coast. There was nothing to do but try to stay on course and ride it out.

All that day and next conditions became steadily poorer, as the ship labored, passing Ocracoke Island and creeping toward Cape Hatteras. With a full gale now blowing, the captain could not set the sails, and had to rely on the engines. Struggling, the ship could only crawl forward. Many clambered into their beds, or found a place to lie down

Hobart decided that staying up on deck was preferable to being below, where poor ventilation did nothing to relieve the stench of sea sick passengers. In the blowing wind, he pulled his sack coat tightly around him and pulled his "lucky" kepi low on his forehead, regretting that he'd left his overcoat at Hart Island.

A soldier – he guessed it was one from the Illinois regiment – staggered up onto the plunging deck. He pushed himself up onto his feet, took a step or two, and collapsed. The water washed over him, and sluggishly he rose to his hands and knees. Lurching rather than crawling, he made it to the side and embraced the railing like a lover. Hobart watched as the boy's torso twisted and heaved.

Poor bugger. Seasick as hell.

He thought back on his last trip and recalled what he'd written to Emma

> … It is the first time I ever was Sea Sick and I hope it will
> be the last. .

He managed the trace of a grin.

I guess that didn't work

He watched the wretched soldier, helpless to combat the rolling of the ship. The youth swayed as the ship hurled side to side. A tendril of saliva hung from his lip, then was torn away in the wind. Finally his arms slid from the railing and he fell on his back, unable to move, the water splashing in his face.

By late on the second day out, they had reached a location somewhere south of Cape Hatteras, but how close to the shore was anyone's guess. Early in the voyage he'd seen the captain hold a pocket anemometer aloft to gauge the wind speed, but now the captain was nowhere to be seen. Winds raged and the waves crested high above the gunwales, relentlessly pounding the thousand-tonner General Lyon as it struggled north. The crew on deck fought gamely, scaling the masts to secure the wildly flapping sails.

Below, the passengers were tossed about without mercy. The children, the women and most of the men stayed in their beds, tying themselves in to avoid being hurled to the deck. Water, vomit and waste coursed through the passages, adding to their misery.

Hobart had experienced rough weather on previous voyages, and he stayed up on deck.

Rather be tossed about. God! It stinks down there!

He thought briefly about hanging on to the railing but shook his head.

A fool's gambit.

He did find a corner by one of the hatches that led below. They were supposed to have been dogged tightly shut, but this one slid back enough to get his head through. Seated at the top of the stairs he could occasionally gulp a breath of air that wasn't sickeningly fetid.

One more day. Just one more day and we'll be in Norfolk.

In the woolen uniform completely soaked by the cold March ocean waters, he shivered. A form crept up beside him. He glanced over – Sergeant Edwards, of the escort party. Several other forms crouched behind him. He shouted something. Hobart shook his head.

"I can't hear you!" He had to holler and wasn't sure he'd been heard. He tried again. Sergeant Edwards leaned in close, shrieking almost into his ear.

"Let's get our guys forward! I think we can get up to the t'gallant fo'c'sle we might stay out of the wind!"

"Where?"

"The fo'c'sle! Up there!" He gestured into the wind, toward the bow of the ship.

Hobart nodded, and the party crept forward on all fours. They huddled in the shelter that the structure, together with the gunwale, provided. While the ship wallowed in the waves, one of the privates cocked his head to one side.

"What's that?"

The others shook their heads.

"Can't hear anything above this wind!"

"No, listen! Don't you hear it?"

They craned their heads. Then, between the howling gusts, they heard it. An insistent, low, rumbling growl. It seemed to come from the leeward side, toward the shore.

"Are those breakers? We aren't supposed to be this close to the shore!" They looked at each other with alarm. Edwards spoke.

"The Captain knows what he's doing, lads. We'll just hunker down here and ride it out. One more day."

Suddenly Hobart caught the sharp, pungent smell of fuel oil.

Kerosene?

A long, narrow tongue of flame stabbed up like a bayonet from a ventilator grate immediately aft of the pilot house. It subsided, then returned, taller and broader. This time it stayed.

"Fire!" a sailor screamed hoarsely. Hobart froze in horror. Behind him, the hatch he'd just left spewed flames onto the deck. A form dove out, engulfed in flames and screaming. More followed, stumbling up the ladder onto the heaving deck, falling over each other as bright, evil, yellow arms of fire reached toward the sky and the thundering storm.

A man rushed from the pilothouse. It might have been one of the officers, but it was impossible to tell in the chaos. He saw the man grab one sailor, then another, and begin to rock the arms of something on deck. A narrow hose snaked from it , and Hobart realized it was a pump. They were feverishly trying to get water to the flames.

Sergeant Edwards screamed at him.

"I'll take Goold and Murphy and go aft! There's boats there! You get as far forward as you can! Find something to keep you afloat if you go over the side. Take Silas and the others with you!" He turned and scrambled toward the stern.

"Come with me!" Hobart roared at the crouching soldiers. Together, they pushed forward, onto the roof of the forecastle.

The ship heeled, his feet flew from under him and he slammed hard onto the wet, wooden deck. Momentarily stunned, he rose to his knees, and could see only what looked like a forest of blazing trees, bursting through the deck wherever there was an opening. The entire ship was on fire, and the thought was terrifying

We're not going to make it. Won't get to Norfolk.

He got shakily to his feet and clutched his head, trying to clear the fog. Perversely, a trail of words, like wispy spiderwebs, wandered through his consciousness:

The boy stood on the burning deck
Whence all but he had fled;
The flame that lit the battle's wreck
Shone round him o'er the dead

Angrily he shook his head and squinted. There was a group of people moving aft toward the stern and, through the flames, a smaller group forward toward the bow. In between, the ship was entirely engulfed in fire, completely covered from rail to rolling rail. He could hear shrieks below.

Heavenly God, they're trapped down there. They're dying.

"A ship! A ship!"

A young man pointed ahead and the starboard side, toward Hatteras. There, distant and only occasionally visible through the driving rain and waves, appeared the masts of one, maybe two ships. As he watched, the Lyon pitched again and he lost them in the storm. He peered through the weather, hoping against hope to see them but, when he did, he realized with sickening dread that they were far too distant to be of much help.

A rattle behind him. Groggy, he saw a lifeboat drift downward toward the water. The boat could easily have carried twenty or thirty, he guessed, but there were far fewer than that aboard. Then, shocked, he watched as the small boat, still moored with one line, swung around beneath the stern, where the propellers thrashed the water. There was a crash of breaking wood, a muffled scream, and then only the sound of the storm.

Flames exploded from every opening, every crack, every ventilator. They moved steadily forward. Hobart grabbed the forestay in his left hand and edged out on the bowsprit. The roaring from the port side, the land side, seemed to grow louder, and he wondered if they might be running aground. He continued further out on the bowsprit, clutching the forestay line.

With a chilling crash, a huge breaker smashed into the ship, heeling it over to port, then slamming it to its starboard side. Hobart slipped on the bowsprit, and felt it vanish from under his feet. Down into the depths the force of the wave crushed him, and he tumbled uncontrollably.

His head broke the surface. He gasped. The General Lyon, now wholly overwhelmed by the fire, was drifting rapidly away. He thrashed wildly, but the sodden weight of his woolen uniform trousers and coat added thirty pounds, and he could do little. Another wave crashed down, and the lucky kepi he'd worn for so long spun from his head and vanished into the murk. He tried to lift his arms to swim. They were leaden. Water filled his nose and mouth, and he went under again. A dim light seemed to flicker above him, but it had become suddenly quiet. The paralyzing chill of the icy water and wind was gone. Now, he felt embraced by a odd and almost peaceful warmth and calm. His flailing slowed.

Twenty-four hours from that moment, the ocean off Cape Hatteras was calm, with only a slow, gentle undulation stirring its surface. The first sun of April coaxed the chill from the air.

155

Nine days from that moment, General Lee, patrician and regal in his dress uniform, rode his famous horse to Appomattox Court House. There, in Wilmer McLean's drawing room, he surrendered the Army of Northern Virginia to a casually uniformed General Grant.

Fourteen days from that moment, the President of the United States died when a bullet shattered his skull.

But at that moment, Corporal Hobart Walker's glazing eyes slowly closed and he sank into the Atlantic's black, icy eternity.

END

Epilogue

The steamship General Lyons sank on March 31, 1865. Records are incomplete, but the final death toll is thought to number between 550 and 600. Only 29 persons were saved, including Sergeant James Edwards, who was part of the escort party from Hart Island. In the days that followed the sinking, the nation's attention was riveted on Lee's surrender to Grant, the end of the war, and the assassination of Lincoln. The loss of the General Lyon, while tragic, was swept aside by the bigger stories. Sergeant Edwards did correspond with Ferdinand Walker, who spent months writing letters, trying to gather Hobart's belongings.

Hobart's body was never recovered, but his name was engraved on the family stone in Greenwood Cemetery in Brooklyn.

Greenwood Cemetery, Brooklyn, NY

Greenwood Cemetery, Brooklyn, NY

About the Author

John Ickes is an unrepentant New Yorker, born in Queens, raised in spite of Long Island, educated "upstate" and a fervent, frothing Mets fan. When high school was over and no one was looking, he escaped, joined the Navy and spent slightly more than a quarter-century as a cryptologist and Surface Warfare Officer. He's left footprints (and probably owes money to people) in Guam, Iceland, Germany, Scotland, Connecticut, Florida, New York, Virginia and any number of ports, exotic and otherwise, around the world.

Once he figured out how much fun education was, he earned an AAS in Hotel Management (thank you, SUNY Delhi), a BA from (what is now) Empire College, and an MA in International Studies from Old Dominion University in Norfolk.

He is inordinately fond of music, particularly Celtic and (thanks to the sainted Jim Petrie) plays bagpipes.

John resides in Virginia Beach, Virginia with his beyond-patient bride of many decades, Vonia. He is the father of Heather (Virginia Beach) and Rebecca (Reading, MA) and the annoyingly proud grandfather of Sage, Keira and Michael.

He is rumored to be housebroken.

In his "A Kepi in the Tide," John Ickes presents us with a gem of a story—and one too incredible to be fiction! The real-life account of Hobart Walker takes us on an unbelievable journey of sacrifice, service, and non-stop adventure as Private Walker goes above and beyond in service to his nation during America's Civil War.

- Jeff Andrews, author of "The Freedom Star"

A Kepi in the Tide brings the Civil War and Hobert Walker to life in a book that is as enjoyable to read as it is rich in history and detail.

Sandy Strehlou

Historic Preservation Review Board

Town of Friday Harbor, Washington

62388174R00105

Made in the USA
Columbia, SC
02 July 2019